The Institute of Biology's
Studies in Biology no. 15

Developmental Plant Anatomy

by *Alan R. Gemmell* Ph.D., F.I.Biol.
Professor of Biology, University of Keele

Edward Arnold

© Alan R. Gemmell 1969

First published 1969
by Edward Arnold (Publishers) Limited,
25 Hill Street,
London, W1X 8LL
Reprinted 1971
Reprinted 1973
Reprinted 1975

Boards edition ISBN: 0 7131 2222 6
Paper edition ISBN: 0 7131 2223 4

Printed in Great Britain by
The Camelot Press Ltd, Southampton

General Preface to the Series

It is no longer possible for one textbook to cover the whole field of Biology and to remain sufficiently up to date. At the same time students at school, and indeed those in their first year at universities, must be contemporary in their biological outlook and know where the most important developments are taking place.

The Biological Education Committee, set up jointly by the Royal Society and the Institute of Biology, is sponsoring, therefore, the production of a series of booklets dealing with limited biological topics in which recent progress has been most rapid and important.

A feature of the series is that the booklets indicate as clearly as possible the methods that have been employed in elucidating the problems with which they deal. There are suggestions for practical work for the student which should form a sound scientific basis for his understanding.

1968

INSTITUTE OF BIOLOGY
41 Queen's Gate
London, S.W.7.

Preface

For many years the anatomy of plants has been presented in a geographical fashion, the student simply learning how to recognize tissues and their geographical distribution in a stem. In recent years plant anatomy has tended to become much more experimental and the focus has moved from simple description to the processes which underlie growth and differentiation. At the same time, light has been thrown on the manner in which many parts of the structure of plants relates to their final function. This book is really about the basic question of biology, namely, problems of differentiation and it is hoped that it will encourage serious students to look on the anatomy of plants with a new understanding and not simply as an exercise in memory.

It might be found useful if teachers of botany used this book as the basis for a tutorial or a class discussion. This is most easily done by reading a chapter per week, then discussing the difficulties and significance of it with the class, and at the same time, using the laboratory periods to familiarize the students with the ordinary histology and anatomy of plant organs.

A.R.G.

Keele, 1968

iii

Contents

Apices and apical growth

1.1 General

One of the characteristics most often used to distinguish plant from animal cells is the possession by the former of a cell wall. In fact a plant cell has been likened to an animal cell in a strait-jacket. In consequence plant cells very early in life tend to assume a permanent form and although in many cases they can revert to a potentially embryonic condition, normally once the semi-rigid or rigid form is attained the plant cell will no longer participate in normal growth and enlargement.

Under these circumstances the growth of plants is dependent on the continued existence of groups of cells which remain, or whose daughters remain, in an embryonic state for long periods of time. Such groups of cells (or even single cells) constitute the actively growing tissues of plants and are grouped under the general name of meristems. Meristems may be intercalary, lateral, or terminal, and may be restricted to the activities of one cell, a small group, or a large number.

The simplest meristem can be seen in a fungal filament where observations of the tip will show that growth of the hypha is the result of the prolongation of the tip cell, followed frequently by the formation of a transverse wall. An easy check on this can be made by watching the tip of a hypha of Mucor over a few hours and noting the distance of the tip from some fixed point such as a side branch.

It is a matter of some importance to realize that even in a simple filament each daughter of the apical cell may remain actively dividing for some time, but whereas the actual continuing meristematic residue will act as such, the other daughter will only contribute additional cells to the filament for a limited period of time. Meristematic activity therefore need not be, and usually is not strictly confined to the apical cell and there may be a *zone* of cell division and meristematic activity although there is only *one* apical cell (Fig. 1–1(a)).

This type of meristem will inevitably produce filamentous growth so long as the walls laid down are transverse. If however the walls arising in the apical cell are laid down obliquely and especially if they intersect each other then a potential for the formation of a flat thallus is created. NEWMAN (1965) in a very good review paper prefers the term 'continuing meristematic residue' to that of 'apical cell' since he maintains that the apical cell is destroyed at each division and there is a continuing meristematic residue and not a single apical cell. While recognizing the force of NEWMAN's argument it is proposed to use the current terminology in the pages that follow.

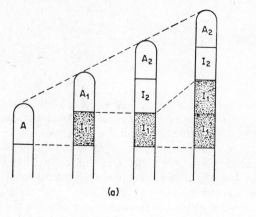

(a)

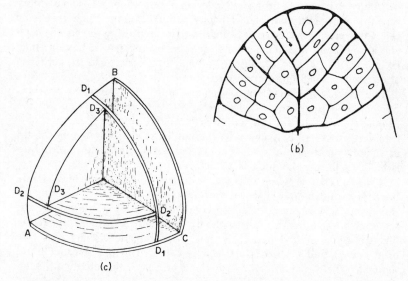

(b)

(c)

Fig. 1-1 (a) *Growth of filaments.* The apical cell (A) divides to form a new apical cell A_1 and a daughter I_1. A_1 may divide again to form A_2 and I_2 and at the same time I_1 may produce two daughter cells. This process may continue for a considerable period showing that growth and division are not limited to the apical cell itself. (b) *Tracing of longitudinal section of fern apex* showing three-sided apical cell and the divisions in the daughter cells. Note the obvious cell lineages which can be distinguished by the thicker walls grouping cells descended from a single daughter cell. (c) *Diagram of a three-sided apical cell* with the curved base facing the reader. First division of this cell is designated D_1D_1, the second division D_2D_2, the third division D_3D_3 and so on. Between successive divisions the meristematic residue grows in size to equal that of the original apical cell A B C.

1.2   The two-or-three-sided apical cell

Strictly speaking to write of such cells as being two-or-three-sided is to perpetuate a misnomer, but usage has sanctified these terms and in consequence they demand explanation. In each case the cell should be regarded as an inverted pyramid, the base of which forms the outer surface of the apex of the plant. Within the plant itself the cell may have two or more faces. If there are two faces then the cell is lenticular in shape, if three such faces the cell is pyramidal (Fig. 1–1(c)). New walls are laid down in regular sequence parallel to the internal walls of the cell and in consequence a regular pattern of division can be seen both in trans- and longisection (Fig. 1–1(b)).

The daughter cells then may undergo successive divisions which result in the establishment of a pattern. Thus in many mosses the leaves are clearly seen to be formed in three rows, each leaf being derived initially from one segment of the three-sided apical cell. Such a system when combined with a multiplicity of division in many planes in the derived cells produces a massive plant body which is at its simplest in the mosses and liverworts and at its most complicated in the vascular cryptogams.

Although the apical cell is so-named by virtue of its position in the plant, its importance lies in its role of initiator of structure. There have been many attempts to explore the physiology of apical cells (WARDLAW 1950, CUTTER 1961) and it has been shown that if the apical cell is destroyed by a fine puncture, there is no regeneration of a new apex but in the apical dome a number of new buds will arise each with its own apical cell.

Finally, a consideration of Fig. 1–1(b) will show that the frequency of division of the apical cell may be lower than that of its derivative daughter cells. Cell lineages can be clearly seen in the section. The synthesis of DNA may be more extensive in the vicinity of the apical cell than in the apical cell itself. This has been demonstrated by using radio-active ^{32}P or ^{14}C and studying its incorporation into newly formed nuclei.

1.3   The complex apex

In 1759 WOLFF recognized the apex as a region from which the rest of the plant seemed to develop. HOFMEISTER and others began to study the apex of the vascular cryptogam in the 1840's and the apical cell was drawn and described by HOFMEISTER in 1857. The precision of division of the apical cell, its size, and the ease with which it could be demonstrated in vascular cryptogams, initiated a period of research into the apex of the flowering plants and it speedily became clear that here the situation was very complex.

The shoot apex of the flowering plant is dome-shaped with leaf primordia arising along the flanks and at the base of the dome. It is not

easy to see definite apical cells and in consequence descriptions of the
plant apex have fallen into three main categories.

1.3.1   *Description based on cell differentiation*

This type of description arises from the work of HANSTEIN in 1868 who
maintained that the plant body arose from three discrete 'histogens'.
Thus, cells derived from the dermatogen would become epidermis, the
periblem would give rise to the cortical tissues, while the plerome would
eventually produce the central stele. In roots, a fourth histogen was
recognized as giving rise to the root cap and was named the calyptrogen
(Fig. 1–2(b)).

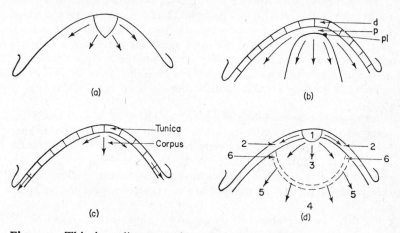

Fig. 1–2   This is a diagrammatic representation of the four systems of
apical growth and description.

(a) A single apical cell. **(b)** The HANSTEIN histogen description which isolates
dermatogen (d) periblem (p), and plerome (pl). **(c)** Tunica-corpus description with anticlinally dividing tunica cells, while those of the corpus divide in
all planes. **(d)** The 'Zones of Growth' description, showing

        (1) apical initials
        (2) mantle layer
        (3) central mother cell zone
        (4) pith
        (5) rib meristems
        (6) zone of cambium-like cells

It was never clear whether HANSTEIN and his co-workers envisaged the
histogens as a row of three cells from which the rest of the plant arose, or
whether each was regarded as a group of initials. Subsequent work, while
tending to remove the element of absolute predestination in the histogen
idea, has in some cases shown patterns of development supporting the

hypothesis. The greatest difficulty in the way of general acceptance of the theory lies in the seeming plasticity of the region where cortex and stele meet, which in some plants may come from putative periblem and in others from plerome.

1.3.2   *Description based on apical geography*

A different approach which sought to overcome the seeming rigidity of HANSTEIN's Histogen Theory was made by SCHMIDT in 1924. He examined the apices of many plants and proposed a method of describing the apex based on the direction of cell division in successive layers. Thus the layer or layers which divided only by walls at right-angles to the surface (anticlinal divisions) was designated the 'tunica' while the rest of the apex in which the cells divided in many planes was called the 'corpus'. The description is therefore called the Tunica-Corpus theory (Fig. 1–2(c)).

It is an obvious conclusion that the tunica by virtue of its anticlinal divisions could only add to the surface layer or layers of the plant and could contribute little to the major part of the plant body. In a 1-layered tunica therefore, SCHMIDT had proposed the equivalent of HANSTEIN's dermatogen. The tunica however may consist of two or three layers and so as well as producing epidermis the tunica may be the site of origin of leaves and of cortical tissues in many cases.

Clearly, the *corpus* is responsible for the production of much of the cortex and the central stele. It includes, therefore, much of the sense of the periblem and plerome, but unlike HANSTEIN's description it does not predict the future of any of its component cells.

If the SCHMIDT description is correct, then there can be no exchange of cells between tunica and corpus and they should be demonstrably discrete. SATINA and his co-workers have developed chimaeras in which layers of different degrees of polyploidy can be seen at the apex and the separateness of tunica and corpus visually demonstrated.

In a tunica-corpus system it is obvious that each layer of the tunica must have a separate initial or group of initials, and it would be expected that a similar initial or group of initials would be required to maintain the corpus. Thus the minimum number of initial cells must be equal to the number of layers of tunica plus one for the tier of corpus initials.

The differences between HANSTEIN's and SCHMIDT's concepts of the apex are not very great, save that the tunica-corpus theory allows for greater plasticity in all the sub-epidermal layers.

1.3.3   *Description based on growth zones*

As a Group the Gymnosperms show a wide variety of apical structure which does not lend itself to simple description. FOSTER in 1943 suggested possible evolutionary trends within the Gymnosperm apex and described a general pattern of development based largely on studies of *Ginkgo biloba* (Fig. 1–2(d)).

There is a group of apical cells some of which by anticlinal divisions give rise to the tunica (Mantle layer of POPHAM 1951, see *Plant Morphogenesis* by SINNOTT 1960). The lowest cells in this initial group however divide periclinally to produce a zone of central mother cells. The latter are of irregular shape and highly vacuolate. In this central mother cell zone the peripheral cells may be very active in division, although those cells in the centre of the zone divide relatively infrequently.

At the base of the central mother cell zone, the dividing cells give rise to the pith and may pass through a period of very active division to constitute rib-meristems. Just outside this is a zone which produces cortex and procambial tissues, while from the surface layers arise the leaf primordia and the epidermis with its appendages.

Such a description of the apex is not nearly so exact as those provided by the histogen or the tunica-corpus statements, but it has the virtue of being very generally applicable. It is also understandable that it may be impossible to describe the apex precisely and in general terms, as the variety in apical growth may only arise from a varying apical situation. FOSTER (1949) suggests that the primitive apex of vascular plants was massive with a large initiation zone, and a substantial core of mother cells. With evolutionary progress the initiating zones became smaller and more clear cut so that a separation of surface and volume growth led to a tunica-corpus system each with its own independent initials.

Evidence is accumulating however that the zonation of cytohistologically differing cells seen in the apex of gymnosperms is still visible under a rigid tunica-corpus system.

1.4   The root apex

In theory roots should be simpler to examine than stems since there is no rapid development of lateral organs such as leaves from a root apex (lateral roots arise from a position in the root far behind the areas in which apical activity is taking place). Roots have therefore proved valuable material in which to study apical structure and physiology and much information has been collected and summarized by CLOWES (1961).

In general the root apex is short and rarely exceeds one millimetre in length. From this apical area arise not only the root of the plant itself, but also the tissues of the root cap or calyptra (Fig. 1–3)*. In many roots there is a clearly marked layering which has led some workers to apply HANSTEIN's histogen theory more readily to roots than to stems. Nevertheless apart from the epidermal layer, there is still the same indefiniteness about the ultimate fates of 'periblem' and 'plerome' as in the stem.

Modern studies have revealed the existence of many different apical patterns which have been provisionally classified by ESAU (1953) on the

* See Fig. 7–1.

basis of the number of initiating layers and the directions in which divisions occur. It is proper, therefore, to talk of an 'initial zone' which may in vascular cryptogams consist of an apical cell, whereas in a higher plant there may be three layers of cells each with its unique pattern of division.

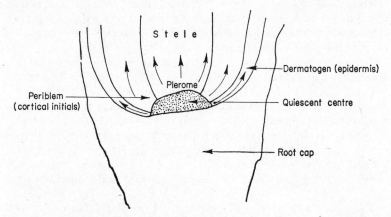

Fig. 1–3   Longitudinal section of root tip based on Fig. 34 from CLOWES, *Apical Meristems*.

The problem has been posed of the size of each initiating layer, is it a single cell per layer or a small number of cells? Work by BRUMFIELD (1943) indicates the existence of one, two or three, apical cells in the root of *Crepis* and *Vicia*. This conclusion was reached by exposing young roots to X-rays and then allowing them to grow. The irradiation caused visible changes in the chromosomes of apical cells and these changes could be recognized in the descendants of the altered apical cells. Examination of such roots revealed that the altered cells gave rise to wedge-shaped sectors which included epidermis, cortex, stele etc. The largest sectors encompassed about one-third of the root, and the most reasonable explanation of this finding is that at the time of irradiation there were probably three apical cells one of which gave rise to the altered sector.

Rather similar evidence has been advanced for stems and it may be that the apical cell or apical cells idea is not so absurd as once was thought for flowering plants.

CLOWES has also shown the existence of a 'quiescent centre' in roots situated between the root cap and a zone of a very active cell division. In the quiescent centre DNA synthesis is very low as also is protein synthesis. Newman argues that if the plant form is to be maintained then there must be a zone where division is infrequent but not absent and this zone, the 'quiescent centre' may be the site of the apical initials (Fig. 1–3).

Apical differentiation

It cannot be emphasized too much that an apex is transient, and as time passes so the apex grows on and leaves behind it cells which go through extremely complex series of divisions and differentiation before assuming their final form. In fact the apex could be defined as part of the plant which destroys itself at each cell division, but from whose destruction new apical cells and the rest of the plant arise.

But the plant body is very much larger and more complex than the apex, therefore behind the apex and its dividing cells, there is a constant adjustment of form and position which must operate in such a way that the new tissues formed at the apex will exactly integrate with those already formed. Or to put it in a more definite way, the new tissues must be so formed that the whole plant will always be a continuous system with vessel accurately abutting on vessel and sieve tube meeting sieve tube.

The nicety with which these adjustments are made have called forth the obvious question of the relationship of the apex to the rest of the plant. In its simplest form, does the apex determine the shape of the plant, or is the apex induced to do things by the tissues already formed? Or do external forces control both? Or is there a continuous interaction between internal and external forces? These and similar questions have been studied for many years but before they can be answered it is essential to have a clear picture of the normal situation in the apex and in the zone immediately behind it.

2.1 Zones of growth

In a series of papers in the *New Phytologist* (1920 *et seq.*) PRIESTLEY describes the types of cell which can be seen in an apex and which represent three stages in the development of a cell. These can be seen in a longisection of any stem or root and although each grades into the subsequent stage they can be described in the following terms.

2.1.1 *Eumeristem* (*true meristem*).

In this area which PRIESTLEY described as the actual apex the cells may vary in size but have a large distinct nucleus and a complete absence of visible vacuoles. The cell walls are thin and their staining reactions are like those of the cytoplasm, a property which may be enhanced by the large number of intercellular connections. As a consequence of the thin walls and absence of vacuoles such eumeristematic cells are plastic and so occupy all the available space in the apex, leaving no intercullular spaces. The eumeristem is regarded by PRIESTLEY as an area of protein synthesis.

More recently much work has been done especially by BROWN and his co-workers (see Symposium of the Society for Experimental Biology (1963) No. XVII *Cell Differentiation*) using modern techniques of cytochemistry, etc., and he states 'At the apex of the root the cells are small, more or less isodiametric, they have thin walls and the body of the cell is occupied with cytoplasm in which a prominent nucleus is embedded.' STRUGGER (1957) estimates that there are thousands of intercellular connections in this area, and an electron microscope photograph by LEECH, MOLLENHAUER and WHALEY (in S.E.B. Symposium 1963) demonstrates this point very forcibly.

2.1.2 *Vacuolated and dividing cells.*

Apart from the continuing meristematic residue, cells of the eumeristem very rapidly pass to the next stage in their development, namely vacuolating and dividing cells. This stage according to PRIESTLEY is characterized by the development of small vacuoles which fuse to form larger vacuoles. WHALEY, MOLLENHAUER and LEECH have followed this process by electron microscopy and believe that in the eumeristem cells there are prevacuolar substances which are utilized and replaced by water to form small vacuoles which eventually fuse.

Obviously cells which are increasingly vacuolate must be expanding and in this zone the expansion is associated with changes in cell wall composition. The middle lamella and the primary cell walls of the eumeristem contain high proportions of pectic substances but, as the wall ages, α-cellulose and hemi-celluloses dominate the chemical scene. Such a wall would be elastic rather than plastic and so intercellular spaces begin to be visible. It must not be assumed that the expansion of these cells is simply a consequence of vacuolation for there is considerable increase not only in size but also in dry weight, DNA, and protein content. Thus the increase in size is a visible demonstration of a changed metabolic state and not simply a sign of water uptake.

If continued division is the criterion of meristematic cells then the vacuolated and dividing cells are probably the most active meristems in the plant for they are found in the mother cell zone and by their repeated division produce much of the primary plant body. If the divisions in a vacuolated dividing cell are parallel to each other, then a file of cells will be produced each of which may continue to divide in the same plane and will constitute a rib meristem. Division in many planes will produce a tissue mass or a mass meristem, while continued anticlinal division will produce a sheet meristem, e.g. a 1-layered tunica.

2.1.3 *Vacuolated extending cells.*

This stage is assumed by PRIESTLEY to be reached by most cells when divisions cease and the cell enlarges to its maximum size. Such cells if they do not differentiate further will become parenchymatous cells whose shape ideally would be isodiametric, but because of restrictions imposed by more rigid barriers, e.g. cuticle, xylem, sclerenchyma, etc., they may vary considerably in shape.

It was thought formerly that vacuolated and extending cells had made their final contribution to plant size and were fully differentiated but it is now realized that most living plant cells are capable of further division and can revert to a very active meristematic status.

2.2 Cellular differentiation

Behind the actual apical regions cells begin to change and assume permanent or semi-permanent forms as they age. This process of differentiation must be mediated by DNA but since cells with the same DNA may eventually have very differing structures and functions one is forced to assume that other factors operate which influence final form. This is the basic problem of differentiation about which little is known that is positive.

Where attempts are made to grow isolated plant cells in suspension culture, the results are very inconclusive. Most of the cells die—in only a few cases do the cells develop into small colonies. Colony formation is increased by introducing a piece of callus tissue into the culture, but is most easily obtained when the culture is started from a small group of cells.

Cells in suspension culture undergo many morphological changes, but few, if any, of these changes could be analogized to the process of differentiation in the growing plant. In many cases giant cells with many nuclei have been found, filaments may be formed which become branched, but anything resembling tracheids or vessels has only been seen very rarely and even then under doubtful conditions (MUIR *et al.* 1958).

The story is different when pieces of tissue are grown in artificial culture.–STEWARD (1964) reports on small (2 mg) pieces of the phloem of carrot which were grown in artificial culture. When gently agitated small pieces of the explant floated free and if furnished with the appropriate food supply could grow to form a spherical nodule within which a root meristem and a shoot initial would arise. This embryonic structure was able to grow into a normal carrot plant.

There is some doubt whether these carrot plants were derived from single cells or from very small but multicellular pieces. The growth of complete plants from small pieces of callus has been known for many years and SKOOG and MILLER (1957) showed that the type of growth could be influenced by varying the concentrations of indole acetic acid and kinetin in the medium. Thus high IAA induced root formation while a high kinetin proportion induced shoot formation.

It would seem therefore from the present evidence that differentiation is essentially a multicellular phenomenon and may necessitate the formation and movement of different chemicals (probably hormones) to and from different cells in the differing multicellular environment (outside, inside, surface restriction on unlimited growth, gravity, etc.) before the organized process of differentiation can proceed.

2.3   The pattern of vascular differentiation

As the cells of the shoot and root apex age and are displaced by their younger descendants, a transection will show clearly that all the cells are not differentiating in the same way (Fig. 2–1(a)). At the periphery the

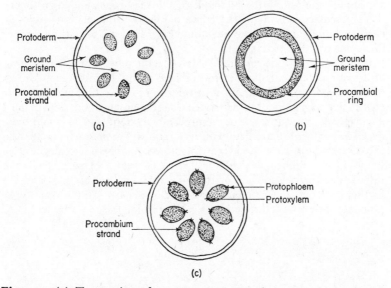

Fig. 2–1   (a) Transection of stem near apex to show protoderm, ground meristem and discrete procambial strands.
(b) As above, but with procambial ring.
(c) Section slightly lower than 2–1(a) showing points of origin of protophloem and protoxylem.

cells are vacuolating, dividing and expanding to form the epidermal system and are named the protoderm. Much of the section is occupied by large highly vacuolated cells which by continued division will form the cortex, pith, and much of the ground tissue. As well as these two zones, a ring of cells can be seen which are smaller and denser, and when viewed in longisection have pointed ends. This is the procambium from which most of the vascular system will arise. In many cases, especially in annuals there is not a complete procambium ring but rather a series of discrete groups or strands of procambial cells forming a circular pattern (Fig. 2–1(a)).

The first cells of the procambium to differentiate are those at the outside. They elongate and undergo an unequal longitudinal division resulting in the production of a large element, the sieve tube member, and an equally long but thin cell, the companion cell (in some cases there may be a number of companion cells formed by successive divisions of the nucleus of the original companion cell).* This area of cells is the protophloem (Fig. 2–1(c)).

A little further away from the apex and at the *inside* of the procambial ring or strands, other differentiating cells can be seen which elongate and differentiate especially by wall thickenings to form tracheids and vessels and are recognizable as the protoxylem. The maturation and formation of these vascular elements at the edges of the procambial tissue may be occurring while the procambium strand itself may still be in the course of formation at other points.

Many terms have been coined to describe the process of differentiation of the vascular tissue from the procambial ring, but the most useful frame of reference is probably obtained by referring to the centre of the stem or root as the fixed point. The first xylem to differentiate in the stem of most angiosperms is in the *inside* of the procambial strand and so is said to be *endarch*. Further differentiation of the strand will therefore be away from the centre and is designated 'centrifugal' xylem. These terms could also be applied to phloem which would then be *exarch* (since it begins to differentiate on the outside of the procambial strand or ring) and the further phloem development would be *centripetal* (Fig. 2–2). Since phloem nearly always differentiates in this fashion the terms are restricted

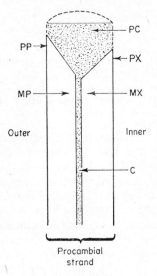

Fig. 2–2 Diagram of longisection of top of procambial strand to show mode of origin and subsequent development of phloem and xylem. Note that protophloem is higher up procambial strand than protoxylem and that the edge of the strand differentiates before the centre. There is frequently an undifferentiated region of the procambial strand which eventually becomes cambium.

PC = procambial strand
PP = protophloem
PX = protoxylem
MP = metaphloem
MX = metaxylem
C   = cambium

* In other cases the protophloem may lack companion cells although sieve tubes may be well developed.

to the xylem and when used appropriately can describe the area in which differentiation begins and the direction in which it proceeds. Thus xylem may be endarch, exarch, or mesarch, and differentiation may be centrifugal, centripetal or both.

It is customary to designate permanent tissues which arise from pro-cambium as primary in contradistinction to those which arise from the vascular cambium and are designated secondary. Of the primary tissues the first formed is given the prefix 'proto' and the tissue developed subsequently is prefixed 'meta'. Thus the following schema can be set up.

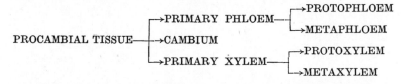

It will be clear that if the primary xylem is exarch, then the proto-xylem will be on the outer limit of the xylem strands and the metaxylem will develop in a centripetal direction (towards the centre).

2.4 Patterns of procambial differentiation

It is well to realize that many problems are involved in the process of stem vascularisation and for present purposes two must be kept rigidly separate, viz.

(1) the origin and development of the procambium itself
(2) the differentiation of the procambium into primary xylem and phloem.

It is the first of these problems which will be considered in this section.

If a shoot apex is examined it can be seen that the procambial strands and those tissues which differentiate from it are associated with the areas in which leaves arise. The question is therefore raised 'Do the leaf primordia induce the formation of procambial tissues or does the upward extension of the procambium (as the apex grows on and cells age) deter-mine the position of the leaves?' (Fig. 2–3).

Observations on the apex of dicotyledons and conifers (ESAU, 1953) show clearly that there is always continuity in procambial strands, there-fore the development must be towards the apex (acropetal). This develop-ment eventually will link the vascular system of the leaf with that of the stem and so there is a certain presumption that the procambial strand as it develops acropetally (i.e. from below towards the apex) determines the position of the leaf on the apical dome of the plant.

It is surprising therefore to discover that when this hypothesis is tested experimentally, the results lead to the opposite conclusion. ALLSOPP (1964) has provided a review of this experimental work. Thus if an apex is exposed, by observing the positions of existing leaf primordia it is possible to forecast very accurately where the next, and yet undeveloped, primordia will arise. WARDLAW (1956) and SNOW and SNOW (1948) operated on the apex and undercut the positions in which future leaf primordia would arise. If the procambium induced leaf formation then the undercut areas

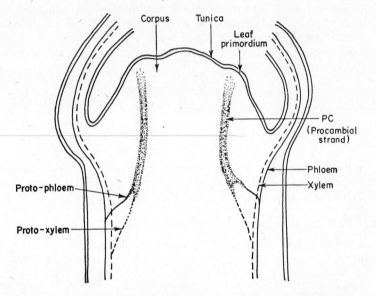

Fig. 2–3 Diagram of longisection of apex of angiosperm showing the extension of the procambial strand towards the leaf primordia and representing the manner in which the strands link up to already existing leaf traces.

should not have developed into primordia and eventually leaves. The undercutting however did not prevent leaves arising in their normal position. Further WETMORE and SOROKIN (cited by ALLSOPP) grafted shoot apices of *Syringa* into undifferentiated callus and showed that in the area flanking the grafted apex, procambium and eventually vascular tissue developed.

It is concluded therefore that although the visible development of procambial strands is acropetal, there is an influence diffusing downwards from the apex and presumably from presumptive leaf primordia which either initiates or directs the development of procambium or both. There is some evidence (see Chapter 3) that this influence is partly hormonal but may also be associated with other factors to which the general name of desmin(s) has been applied.

3.1 The formation of xylem and phloem

The course of differentiation of procambium from the apex and ground tissue has been described in Chapter 2, now the second problem will be considered, namely, differentiation within the procambium itself. In this connection two series of experiments are of significance, the first is by WETMORE and SOROKIN (cited by ALLSOPP 1964) in which shoot apices of *Syringa* when grafted into callus tissue induced not only the development of procambium and also the differentiation of xylem and phloem from this procambium. They also found that some xylem differentiation could be induced in callus tissue if a mixture of auxin and coconut milk was supplied.

An extension of similar work by JACOBS and his colleagues showed that there was a close relationship between the amounts of auxin which diffused from a leaf and the rate of production of xylem elements at the base of the petiole.

The second line of approach has been studied by WETMORE and RIER (see TORREY 1967) who showed that the differentiation of procambial tissue to form xylem or phloem could be strongly influenced not only by the presence of auxin but also by the concentration of sugar present in the medium. Thus it is concluded that differentiation from the procambial strand is probably under the dual control of (a) auxin (or similar substances) diffusing in a basipetal (i.e. from apex to base) direction from the leaf or leaf bud and (b) sugars or other nutrients being transported up the stem in the existing phloem or xylem.

It is clear from the work of WETMORE and RIER that low glucose and high auxin will promote xylem differentiation while high sugar will encourage the differentiation of phloem. Thus since the phloem is the pathway of sugar movement, the appropriate condition for phloem differentiation could be expected to occur at the distal end of existing phloem tissue, and so the path of differentiation of phloem would be acropetal.

3.2 The geography of primary tissues in the stem

The simple distribution of primary tissues within a stem is so fully described in all text-books of botany that only the briefest account will be given here in order to make plant development a connected story (Fig. 3–1).

The boundary layer of all simple primary stems is the epidermis. Depending on the nomenclature adopted this is derived from the outermost layer of the tunica, or the dermatogen, or the protoderm or the mantle layer. Usually the epidermis is only one cell in depth but multiple epidermises are known (e.g. in the leaf of *Ficus*). On the outer epidermal surface there is always a protective barrier of a fatty substance known as the cuticle.

Within the epidermis is a zone of large living cells with few contents. This zone is the cortex and because of its simple structure it is often the

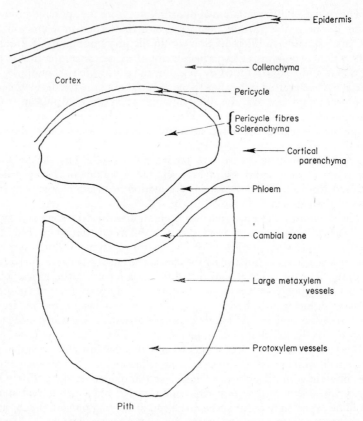

Fig. 3–1   A rough diagram of part of a transection of sunflower (see Plate 1).

zone where starch and other storage products accumulate. Sometimes such cells may be strengthened by additional cellulose wall thickening in which case they are designated collenchyma, or the thickening may be lignin and tissue so thickened is termed sclerenchyma. Lignin is a complex of chemicals which is largely impervious to water and in consequence sclerenchymatous cells are usually dead, while collenchymatous cells are alive and can revert to meristematic activity.

The most obvious features of the transection of a stem are the vascular bundles or the vascular ring. This has three main elements (1) the phloem consisting of vertically elongated cells, the sieve tubes, each with its companion cell or cells (2) the xylem which also consists of vertically elongated cells with thickened lignified walls (each cell becomes a vessel or trachea element and the degree and pattern of thickening has significance) and (3) the undifferentiated procambium which remains between the xylem and phloem and is now designated cambium proper. This cambium retains its meristematic properties almost indefinitely.

In the centre of the stem is another parenchymatous storage area, the pith. Plate 1 shows a photograph of a transection of part of a simple stem as described above and Fig. 3–1 is a diagram of that photograph.

3.3 Primary tissues and functional units

Only plants whose primary structure is well suited to resist selective forces will survive, and in consequence there is a danger that a purpose or a function may be read into a given tissue without evidence to support the idea. For example, for many years the cuticle was considered to be a waterproof barrier whose function was to prevent surface epidermal cells and internal tissues from becoming desiccated.

There is now excellent evidence to show that the cuticle is not quite so continuous or waterproof as early workers had believed for plants can absorb not only water but also substances such as iron or even weedkillers through the surface of the stem and leaves.

Nevertheless, the completeness of the cuticle on the aerial parts of the plant and its almost total absence from the root, lends support to a belief in its protective nature, as also does the thickness of the cuticle in desert plants and its thinness in hydrophytes or plants growing under very moist conditions.

In plants which live for many years it is important that areas of food storage should be developed especially if the plant is deciduous or dies down during the winter. Modified underground parts of swollen stems are sometimes used but in most cases the food is stored in non-soluble form in living cells in the cortex or pith where it can be made soluble when required and transported to the plant meristems when growth is resumed in the spring.

In young actively growing plants the efficient conduction of water and mineral salts throughout the plant is essential and the xylem and phloem are the channels used for this purpose. In the phloem, sieve tubes (Fig. 3–2) are the pathway through which larger molecules (sugars, amino acids etc.) move, although the exact mechanism of translocation is not yet clear. The general opinion is that this mechanism uses metabolic energy and that there is both a relatively slow and a very fast movement. In the xylem water, and its contained salts, may be moved by the action of a root pressure, but for most of the growing season the moving force is a tension from above drawing water up the stem.

Xylem cells are frequently under negative pressure for as water is drawn up the stem by the leaves there develops a tension which unless the xylem were strengthened would produce a flattening or a collapse of the cells. This is avoided by the lignified thickening which not only covers the original cellulose walls but also penetrates into the walls, and obscures the cellulose framework.

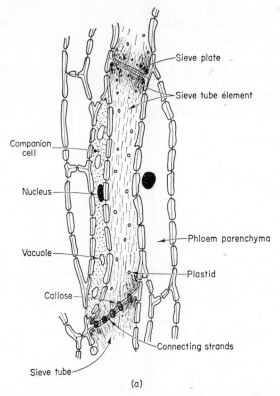

(a)

Fig. 3–2 (a) Drawing of young primary phloem showing sieve tube elements, companion cell, phloem parenchyma, etc. (Based on Fig. 7.18 from 3rd Edition of ROBBINS, WEIER and STOCKING, *Botany: an introduction to plant science*).

In the young actively-growing parts of a plant a rigid, dead xylem cell with thick lignified walls would tear away from the rapidly elongating tissues around it. This danger is reduced in the youngest protoxylem elements for lignification is laid down in a spiral or annular pattern, so that the cellulose wall between the lignin rings or spirals is capable of stretching and the conduction of water to the tip of the plant is assured. Xylem elements produced from procambium lower down the stem where elongation has ceased have their walls completely lignified save for pits which connect adjacent segments. (Plate 2).

Stems containing only primary tissues are relatively weak and in a high wind would easily be broken or at least put under severe stress. An examination of the stem of a number of herbaceous species, e.g. dead nettle, reveals that groups of cells differentiate into fibres with thick lignified walls. These fibre bundles are usually located around the perimeter of the cortex and add strength and rigidity to what might otherwise be a very delicate system.

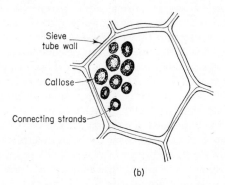

(b)

Fig. 3-2 **(b)** View of sieve plate showing callose surrounding the connecting strands (Based on Fig. 7.18 from 3rd Edition of ROBBINS, WEIER and STOCKING, *Botany: an introduction to plant science*).

It is often found that cortical cells adjacent to the external side of the phloem may also become lignified and are termed pericycle fibres. The advantage of such a lignified system is obvious for sieve tubes are thin-walled and if they were crushed or even slightly compressed they would close and the whole food-conducting system of the plant would be blocked. The pericycle fibres therefore have a protective function.

A comparison of sections of young stems with diagrams and photographs illustrating this chapter will clarify the geography of primary stems, and an examination of the products of maceration of young stems of such plants as cucumber, marrow, etc., will impart a three-dimensional picture of the detailed histology.

Formation of secondary tissues 4

4.1 Origin of vascular cambium

It will be recalled that at the apex in the procambial strands or ring, differentiation of protophloem and protoxylem begins at the outer and inner edges respectively in normal angiosperms. There are therefore two waves of differentiation passing towards the centre of the procambial tissue and if they meet, as they do in many monocots, then the whole procambial strand will become primary vascular tissue. In many cases however these waves do not meet and a zone of original procambial meristematic cells remains. This zone, situated between xylem and phloem is the vascular cambium and, if it is not continuous *ab initio*, by dedifferentiation of parenchymatous cells between the vascular strands it will eventually form a continuous ring of tissue in the stem. From this cambial ring all the secondary vascular tissue of the normal plant will be formed.

The cambium forms a sheath of actively dividing cells which extends from near the shoot apex to near the root tip, and the products of the division of the cambium are usually referred to as secondary tissues. It is plain that there is little hard and fast distinction to be drawn between primary and secondary vascular tissues as it is impossible to say where procambium stops being such and can properly be designated vascular cambium.

4.2 Form of cambial tissue and patterns of division

The vascular cambium contains two distinct types of meristematic cell named repectively fusiform and ray initials. The fusiform initials (Fig. 4–1) are long with pointed ends and owe their name to the spindle shape they show in tangential section. The ray initials on the other hand are isodiametric and relatively small (Fig. 4–1). (Plate 3).

As their name implies the ray initials produce those cells which will eventually be the vascular rays. All the other cell types found in the secondary xylem and phloem are the products of fusiform initials. From the shape of the initials it would seem logical that those cells which extend vertically in the stem, such as vessels, tracheids, sieve tubes etc., should be products of fusiform initials, while those structural elements which extend radially are produced by ray initials (Fig. 4–1).

Microscopically the initials have thin walls which are so highly pitted that they have a beaded appearance. They are highly vacuolate and there is an abundance of protoplasmic connection between the cells. Their nuclear behaviour may also be unusual for it is not too difficult to show that the young xylem elements have highly polyploid nuclei (see DARLINGTON and BRADSHAW (1963) for details of method).

The dominant feature however to which they owe their importance is their continued division in a tangential plane producing secondary xylem to the inside and secondary phloem to the outside thereby increasing the girth of the plant and building up the typical tree structure. Although it is thought most likely that there is a single row of cambial cells, a

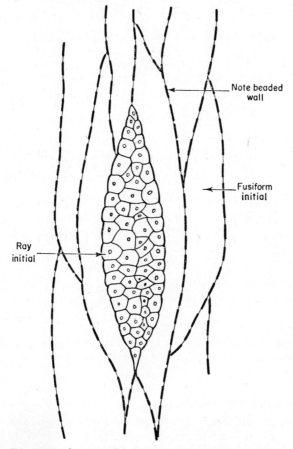

Note beaded wall

Fusiform initial

Ray initial

Fig. 4–1 Diagram of tangential longisection showing fusiform and ray initials.

transection of any growing stem will reveal a cambium *zone* formed by the continued division of the daughter cells formed by the cambium proper (Fig. 4–2).

Here too is NEWMAN's (1965) 'continuing meristematic residue' ideally displayed for when a cambium cell divides tangentially to form two cells, one of the daughters will differentiate and become secondary xylem or phloem while the other will retain its meristematic properties. Potentially therefore cambial division is limitless.

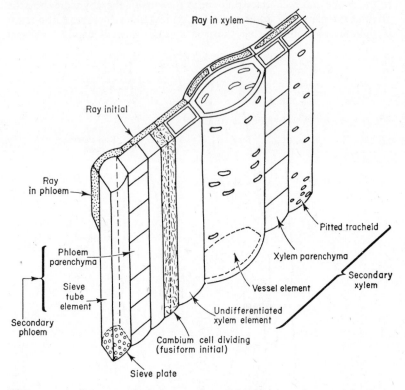

Fig. 4–2 A diagrammatic interpretation of the division of ray and fusiform initials to form secondary xylem and secondary phloem elements (Based on Fig. 7.9 from RAY, *The Living Plant*).

4.3 Problems of cambial growth

It is very difficult indeed to form a three-dimensional picture of what is happening in this cambial area. It is clear however that as the cambium continues to divide it is being displaced or is really displacing itself further from its original position near the centre of the plant. It is therefore forming an ever-increasing perimeter to the secondary xylem and this can only be done either by cambium initials becoming tangentially stretched or by the occurrence of radial divisions producing more cambial initials. At the same time the vertical continuity of the vascular system and the radial continuity of the rays must be maintained.

Data on the first of these points were obtained by BAILEY in 1923 and are summarized in Table 1.

Table 1

		Diameter in μ		
Age of axis	Kind of initial	Vertical	Radial	Tangential
1	Ray	22·9	17·8	13·8
1	Fusiform	870·0	4·3	16·0
60	Ray	24·8	26·6	17·0
60	Fusiform	4,000·0	6·2	42·4

The ray initials have changed very little over 60 years growth, if anything they have become larger in every dimension, but the fusiform initials have increased enormously in vertical and tangential diameter and by about 50 per cent in radial diameter. The conclusion seems obvious that the rays act as fixed points changing but little as continued growth occurs and the increasing perimeter of the tree is taken up by tangentially expanding fusiform initals which surprisingly are not becoming stretched and therefore thinner radially but are expanding radially also.

BAILEY has also calculated the number of ray and fusiform initials at a sixty-year interval and finds that the fusiform initials increase in number from 724 to 23,100 and ray initials from 70 to 8,796. This increase in number of fusiform initials is partly accounted for by their great increase

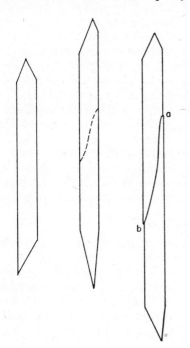

Fig. 4–3 Diagram of pseudo-transverse division in a fusiform initial. By the gradual extension at points (**a**) and (**b**) the two daughter cells will eventually lie side by side.

in length and therefore their intrusion between existing initials. This adds considerably to the number which can be seen in transection, but there remains a residue which can only be accounted for by a radial or similar division of the fusiform initials. This type of division has been seen (BANNAN 1953) and consists of a pseudotransverse wall and then growth of the daughter cells so that they come to lie side by side in a tangential plane (Fig. 4–3).

New ray initials arise by the tip of a fusiform initial being separated from the rest of the cell by a cross wall. This part of the cell undergoes a series of division as a result of which a group of isodiametric cells is produced. These are the ray initials.

This continuous and subtle rearrangement of cells in a mature stem, e.g. a tree trunk, poses great problems of cellular readjustment. For example, tracheids are often larger than the fusiform initials from which they arose. They must therefore interpenetrate previously existing cells and in turn must have their own relationship with their immediate neighbours altered by other elongating cells. To explain this complex situation PRIESTLEY (1930) used the concept of symplastic growth in which the rays because of their radial continuity acted as fixed points and the other cells readjusted their positions mutually, like an expanding elastic trellis in which the fixed points are the areas where the cross-members of the trellis-work are nailed together.

This concept avoided the difficulty of the disruption of protoplasmic connections between adjacent cells following any form of intrusive growth. It was nevertheless a very difficult process to visualize and slowly evidence began to accumulate that interpenetration of an elongating cell between pre-existing cells did in fact occur. This process is named intrusive growth and is well established by the work of BANNAN (see ESAU 1953) who demonstrated that elongating cells grow at the tips. The primary walls of adjacent cells are changed by the advancing tip and become separated either being forced apart by the advancing tip or leaving a space into which the advancing tip will grow. This process necessarily disrupts the intercellular connections between the separated cells but these are re-established between the intrusive cell and those around it. In consequence pit pairs as commonly seen in Gymnosperms always register with each other.

4.4 Periodicity of cambial growth

A comparison of transection of twigs cut at different times of year reveals that cambial activity is stopped or is at a minimum in winter. It begins in spring (the ease with which bark will slip when twisted in early spring is evidence of the presence of many thin walled cambium cells or derivatives), rises to a maximum and then usually comes to an end in late summer. A further result of seasonal periodicity can be seen in the thickness of the walls of secondary xylem vessels or tracheids, for these are thin in early wood and thick in late wood, while early vessels are large but in late wood the vessels are small or may be replaced by tracheids (Plate 4).

In many trees cambial activity begins in the twigs and spreads down the tree to the trunk and WAREING (1951) has related this wave to the formation and distribution of auxin in the spring. The auxins have been shown to be formed in growing buds and they appear at successively lower levels in the tree. It has also been shown that twigs from which the buds have been removed will form 'snags', dry up and die. Application of auxin paste to decapitated twigs will restore cambial growth and may even influence the size and type of cells into which the cambial derivatives may change.

The total effect may be more complex, for in ring-porous trees (such as Oak) WAREING has suggested that there is a reserve of auxin in the cambium through the winter which induces the formation of large wide vessels (hence ring-porosity) at a very early stage of bud development. The application of gibberellic acid to decapitated twigs induces cambial division but good xylem formation is induced only when gibberellic acid and indole-acetic acid are applied together. LOOMIS and TORREY (1964) have used a technique which involved applying glass vials containing various substances to the cut ends of cultured isolated radish roots and have shown that secondary thickening can be induced by supplying sucrose, 6-benzylaminopurine (a kinin) and indole-acetic acid. This growth could be increased by adding m-inositol to the vial, but it did not continue indefinitely indicating that some other factors are involved in the process.

The final problem of why cambial derivatives should become phloem on one side but xylem on the other is largely unresolved. There are many observations and a few experiments which indicate that pressure and possibly gravity have an effect on differentiation. This can be verified by examining bent branches or by looping a flexible twig when it will be found that after a period of growth there is a difference in cell wall thickness and in cell size on the differing sides of the twig. A nice example of this effect is cited by SINNOTT (1960) in which a tree was held by wires so that it could not sway below 20 ft above the ground but could sway freely above this point. The unswayed portion stayed thin as opposed to the thick strong stem which formed above 20 ft. When the wires were removed the situation righted itself by increased growth and differentiation in the part previously held immobile.

There is a consensus (SINNOTT 1960) that the first cambial divisions in the spring produce sieve tubes. Later, xylem is developed at a greater rate than phloem, but as xylem production slows down in the summer a new wave of phloem development occurs which produces a type of sieve tube with a smaller diameter than that of sieve tubes produced earlier in the season.

Secondary tissues 5

5.1 Secondary xylem structure and evolution

The secondary xylem cells can be classified into three main groups (a) the vascular rays which have radial extension, (b) the vertically extended cells such as vessels, tracheids, fibres, etc., and (c) the xylem parenchyma. It will be recalled that the first arises from ray initials and the latter two groups from fusiform initials. A student can gain much insight into the three-dimensional aspect of secondary tissues by cutting a thick twig or a block of wood in the three principal planes, transverse, radial and tangential, and examining the cut surfaces with a hand lens. It is also a useful exercise to try to determine how a board, such as the door of a laboratory cupboard was orientated in the tree from which it was cut.

5.1.1

(a) Ray initials are essentially isodiametric (see Chapter 4) and the first-formed daughter cells will accordingly have the same shape and arrangement. Thus a short vertical series of ray initials will produce a uniseriate ray while a large group of initials more than one cell wide in the tangential plane will give rise to a multiseriate ray (Fig. 4–1). It should never be forgotten that the ray initials are forming ray tissue to the exterior of the cambial ring as well as to the interior, so that a ray does not end at the cambium but begins there and grows in two directions.

It is a matter of common observation that ray cells in the phloem are larger than those in the xylem and it is thought that this is the result of decreased pressure towards the outside of an expanding cylinder when the force producing the expansion is located internally (Plate 5).

It is usual for rays in the secondary xylem to be composed of parenchymatous cells, elongated radially. Thus the number of divisions of the ray initials in any given year may be less than that of the fusiform initials, although the amount of interpenetration of the vertically extending xylem elements makes direct comparisons difficult. Some rays however may develop cells of a different shape along their margins, and these cells may be tracheidal with thickened walls or parenchymatous in nature. Such rays are heterogeneous and are common, e.g. in Scots Pine or Mahogany. Ray cells communicate with secondary xylem tissues by means of pits (Fig. 5–1, Plates 6 and 7).

An examination of fossil and modern woods leads to the conclusion that uniseriate homogeneous rays are primitive and the multiseriate, heterogeneous condition is a derived state, e.g. Pine compared with Oak or Beech.

5.1.2

(b) Cells derived from fusiform initials often elongate (see Fig. 5–3) and may ultimately form long thick-walled xylem fibres or tracheids with lignified walls containing pits showing varied degrees of elaboration.

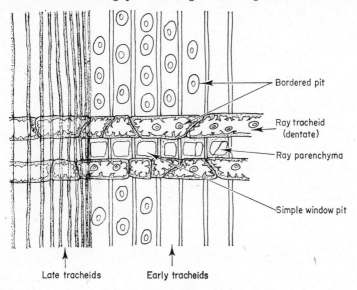

Fig. 5–1   Diagram of Plate 6.

Thus the bordered pit (Fig. 5–2) with an elaborate movable torus can respond to changes in pressure and so restrict the passage of water or solvents in a radial direction. Such fibres and tracheids are formed usually in summer in Angiosperms and because of their small transverse diameter and thick walls constitute a definite ring of hard tissue, the late wood.

In Gymnosperms only tracheids are formed, but late tracheids have much thicker walls than early wood, so that although there are no vessels, annual rings can plainly be seen in most cases. In many flowering plants however (Oak and Ash) the derivatives of a fusiform initial in the spring will stay short and expand in the transverse diameter to form ultimately a vessel segment. Such segments have almost transverse end-walls which disintegrate as the cell matures leading to the death of the cell. As the tree grows, a vertical series of such vessel segments forms a continuous tube through the tree and acts as a pathway through which water and dissolved salts may flow easily upwards from the root.

The lateral expansion of these spring wood vessels crushes adjoining cells and the neat radial rows of cambial derivatives seen in the Gymnosperms is not at all evident in Angiosperms.

A study of vessels and tracheids has led many workers to conclude that the tracheid is the primitive structure found in fossil timbers. The process of evolution has operated to do three things (a) to shorten the tracheids until they are scarcely longer than the fusiform initials from which they

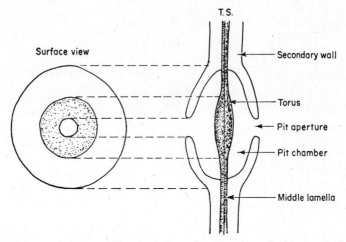

Fig. 5–2   Diagram of surface view of transection of a bordered pit.

arose (b) to extend them in a radial direction to form large wide vessels, and (c) to increase the degree of pitting on the transverse horizontal walls to such an extent that in the modern trees with broad open vessels the cross-walls have been eliminated (Fig. 5–3).

From fusiform initials xylem parenchyma cells may also be formed. These are normal living parenchymatous cells which form a network among the vessels and tracheids and connect with the rays. Thus the tree is permeated with living cells and in the winter if a section of a twig of a deciduous tree is cut and mounted in iodine it will be seen that the rays and the xylem parenchyma are stained blue indicating that these

---

Plate 1. (opposite) Transverse section of stem of sunflower. This section is represented diagrammatically in Fig. 3–1.

Plate. 2. (opposite) Longisection of part of bundle of *Helianthus* showing (a) annular protoxylem (b) pitted metaxylem (c) xylem fibres (d) cambial area (e) phloem with sieve tube and sieve plate.

Plate 3. (opposite) Tangential section of wood of Mahogany showing heterogeneous rays, xylem fibres and tracheids. Note the large border cell at the top and bottom of the rays.

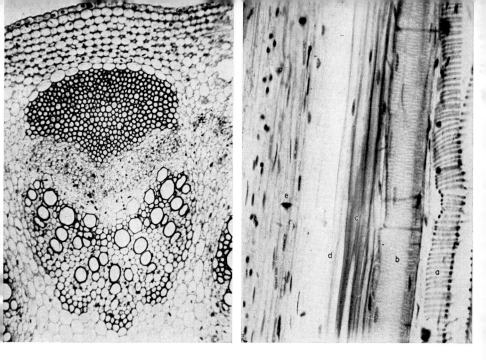

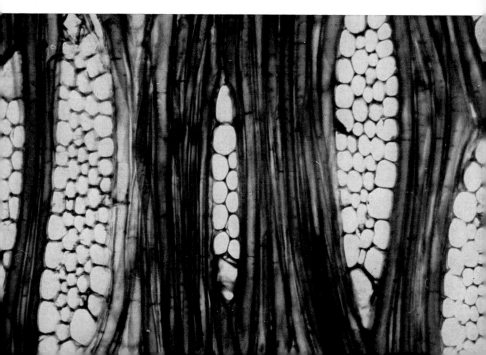

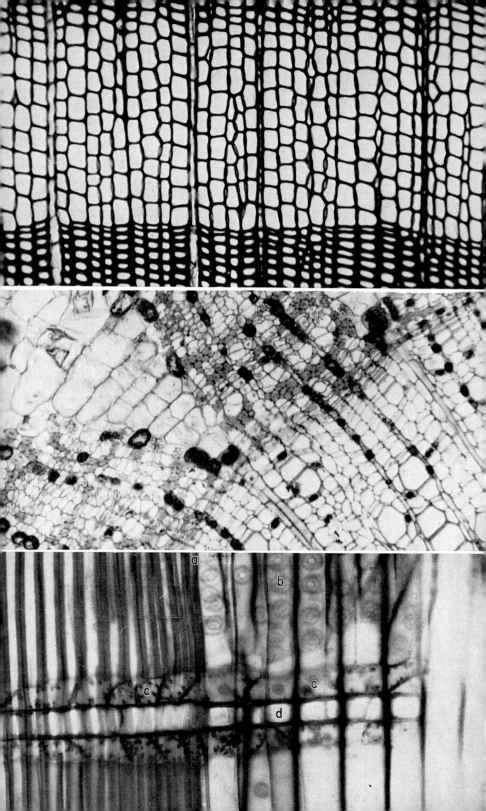

cells are used for starch storage. A similar section cut in late spring would reveal that the starch had been hydrolysed and moved to other parts of the plant to assist in growth.

In many trees and therefore many timbers, the distribution of parenchyma among the vessels and tracheids is not random or diffuse for there are obvious concentrations of xylem parenchyma. Thus in Ash or more easily in Iroko (of which most laboratory benches are made) the trans-

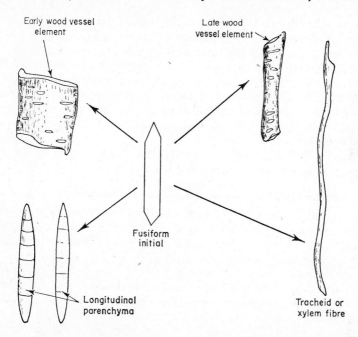

Early wood vessel element

Late wood vessel element

Fusiform initial

Longitudinal parenchyma

Tracheid or xylem fibre

Fig. 5–3   Diagrammatic representation of the changes which may take place in the derivatives of a fusiform initial as they mature.

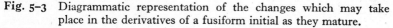

Plate 4. (opposite) Transverse section of stem of *Pinus* showing thick walled late tracheids and the abrupt change to thin walled early tracheids. In the section uniseriate rays are also visible.

Plate 5. (opposite) Part of the transection of a lime stem showing the manner in which the ray parenchyma cells are very much enlarged in the region of the secondary phloem.

Plate 6. (opposite) Radial longitudinal section of wood of *Pinus silvestris* showing (**a**) the change from late to early wood (**b**) bordered pits in surface view (**c**) a ray with external dentate ray tracheids (note small border pits) (**d**) the ray parenchyma with window pits.

verse face of the timber cut with a razor blade or sharp knife will show clear zones of xylem parenchyma around the vessels. This is *paratracheal* parenchyma. In Iroko where the zones flow together it is named *confluent* parenchyma (Plate 8). In true Mahogany (*Swietenia mahogani*) a clear band of parenchyma can be seen at the end of each year's growth, and it is naturally named *terminal* parenchyma. In the dark background of Walnut the *diffuse* parenchyma can be seen as small lighter flecks among the vessels and tracheids when viewed through a × 10 lens.

The strength and decorative value of timbers such as Oak, Mahogany, Plane, Sycamore, etc., is dependent on many of the structural features outlined above. Thus the large early vessels and broad rays of Oak impart its decorative appearance as a carpentry timber, while a diffuse porous timber with thin narrow rays and small uniform vessels such as Sycamore or Maple produces a timber of even strength and no obvious lines of weakness. This type of wood can be used for flooring or for chopping blocks where it is important that wear will be even and there will be no splinters.

A great deal of timber anatomy and identification can be studied with a hand lens and a sharp knife using known samples.

5.2 Secondary phloem structure and evolution

In a fashion similar to the secondary xylem, the secondary phloem contains elements which are vertically elongated and which function for conduction of soluble and not so soluble materials. The most important of these elements is the sieve tube which in angiosperms is usually accompanied by companion cells. The sieve tube is derived from a cambium fusiform initial and in angiosperms it divides in the longitudinal plane to cut off the future companion cells. Sometimes the immediate derivative of the initial may divide transversely or obliquely to form smaller cells each of which may subdivide further to form sieve tube and companion cells. It is usual for those cells destined to become sieve tube members to expand transversely as they diverge from the cambium and consequently there is often little evidence of radial arrangement in the phloem.

The structure characteristic of phloem is the sieve plate or sieve area. These are areas on the common wall between adjacent cells where there are many pits through which protoplasmic connections extend. Thus the sieve areas are analogous to the primary pit fields found in xylem. In Gymnosperms the sieve areas are distributed over all the cell walls and the phloem here is said to consist of sieve cells since they do not form a connected tube. In angiosperms however there is an increasing tendency for the sieve areas to be concentrated on the horizontal walls, so that a vertical tube is formed only interrupted by the highly perforated cross walls or sieve plates (Fig. 3–2).

In 1939 ESAU described phloem sieve tubes as having four developmental stages (a) young stage (b) mature stage (c) transitional stage and

(d) degenerate stage. The sieve tube begins as a living cell with actively streaming cytoplasm and with dense cytoplasmic connections between adjacent sieve tube members. As the cell ages starch and slime begin to accumulate especially at the transverse walls, the nucleus disappears and streaming stops. The cell is now 'mature' and this stage is characterized by a continued thickening of the walls and an accumulation on the sieve plates of a material known as callose which constricts the connecting strands. Such continued deposition changes the appearance of the sieve plate from a thin perforated wall to a thickened wall traversed by rather indefinite connecting strands.

In the transitional stage the sieve tube element is at the end of its active life and the protoplasm completely disorganizes. The callose may then separate from the sieve plate area and be used, possibly as a respiratory substrate, for it too disappears. The sieve plate now is easily seen as a highly perforate cross-wall, but the cell is in the degenerate stage and is easily crushed. Sieve tubes have therefore a short functional life and it seems likely that this may be less than one season.

Considerable research has been done on the physiology of phloem cells and the mechanism of transport of many complex substances, e.g. virus particles, has been extensively studied, but no generally satisfactory theory has been advanced which will explain (a) the speed of phloem transport (b) the fact that it can transport materials in two directions simultaneously (c) its stoppage when acted on by poisons (d) the passage of the materials through the sieve plates.

It is thought by some, that in this admittedly complex process, it is unwise to forget that the phloem contains not only sieve tubes but also companion cells associated with each sieve tube. The relationship appears to be intimate for the separating wall between companion cell and sieve tube member is very thin and often highly pitted. Although as has been indicated above the sieve tube element matures and changes, the companion cell remains remarkably stable and retains its nucleus all its life. It possesses heavily streaming protoplasm and it has been suggested that the companion cell may exert a physiological influence over the sieve tube element and be responsible for structural, etc., changes in that element after its own nucleus has degenerated (ESAU, et al 1957).

Electron microscope photographs reveal that the individual sieve tube elements contain very few mitochondria and practically no other organelles. There is little distinction between vacuole and cytoplasm and the whole cell is filled with the slimy material. In distinct contrast the companion cells are packed with easily visible cytoplasm containing large numbers of mitochondria, ribosomes, plastids, etc., and the endoplasmic reticulum is very highly developed. Such information lends evidence to the view that the sieve tube is largely passive and the companion cells are the energy-producing and directing part of the phloem transport system.

There is a considerable development of fibres in the phloem and numerous parenchyma cells are always present. The latter grade into companion cells and show similar staining properties. In plants which have no companion cells in the phloem, e.g. *Pinus* it is probable that the role of these cells is taken over by phloem parenchyma and it has been suggested that the phylogenetic origin of companion cells is from phloem parenchyma originally casually associated with the sieve tube elements.

Leaves 6

6.1 Origin of leaves and phyllotaxis

The leaf originates by the periclinal division of a group of cells on the flanks of an apical meristem. In angiosperms there is no uniformity in the site of the divisions but generally they occur in the layers below the outermost layer of the tunica although in some monocots even the outermost layer may contribute to the internal tissues of the leaf. The study of periclinal chimaeras has shown that the external tissues of the stem will constitute the epidermis of the leaf, but depending on the number of cell layers in the tunica, the internal tissues of the leaf may arise from either tunica or corpus layers.

Continued local periclinal divisions produce a protuberance on the apical dome, which is called the leaf primordium. The youngest primordium is of course nearest to the apex and as the apex grows on and the primordium ages so it develops the typical leaf form (Plate 9).

Many and elaborate studies have been made of the position of leaf primordia on the apex for these positions determine the phyllotaxis of the leaves. The phyllotaxis of a shoot is determined by tracing a line from a given leaf to that leaf vertically above it, with the line touching the base of all intervening leaves. This can easily be done with thread. It is then found that the leaves are arranged spirally and a mathematical expression of phyllotaxis can be devised by counting the number of times the spiral goes round the stem and the number of leaves passed until the appropriate one is reached. Thus a common phyllotaxis is one where in passing from a given leaf to that directly above it, the stem is circled twice and the fifth leaf is reached. This is written as 2/5 phyllotaxis. Other common values are 3/8, 5/13, and in cones, 8/21, 13/34, etc.

Mathematically such fractions arranged as a series read 2/5, 3/8, 5/13, 8/21, 13/34 where the numerator and the denominator of any member of the series are the sums of the two preceding numerators and denominators, and is known as a Fibonacci series. Such a series tends to a limit which is reached at 0·38197. Expressing this value as a fraction of 360°, the angle between 2 successive leaves projected on a plane surface would be 137° 30′ 28″ the so-called ideal angle. Leaves set at this angle should never be directly above each other.

If the above brief analysis is correct it should be possible to see vertical rows of leaves, but in compressed shoots such as cones of *Pinus*, it can easily be seen that there are no straight lines (orthostichies) but rather spirals (Plate 10). Two sets of spirals can be seen, the first turning clockwise and the other anticlockwise and these are termed parastichies. If these parastichies are expressed mathematically as a fraction by making the number of counterclockwise spirals the denominator and the number of clockwise spirals the numerator, a fresh Fibonacci series is produced of 2/3, 3/5, 5/8, 8/13, 13/21. . . . This series approaches 0·61803 which is the other part of the 'golden mean'. Thus 0·61803 + 0·38197 = 1 and the relationship 0·38197 : 0·61803 = 0·61803 : 1. This is the numerical solution of a well-known problem: 'to divide a line in two parts such that the relationship between the smaller and the greater part is the same as the relationship between the larger part and the whole line.'

This peculiar mathematical relationship of phyllotaxis has long been the subject of speculation and experiment, and it is the experimental work which is described in the next section.

6.2   Experimental work on the apex

Two basic problems have been studied, namely,

(1) why should organs such as leaves arise in this definite phyllotaxis? and

(2) Why should the apex bear leaves and not branches?

It is possible (ALLSOPP 1964) to operate surgically on the apex and by alteration of the position of apical structures to examine the consequent effects on phyllotaxis. If a very young primordium is removed as was done by the SNOWS (1952) it is clearly seen that subsequent primordia are not displaced. Thus a theory advanced by SCHOUTE that a primordium prevented or inhibited the development of further primordia in its immediate vicinity ('field' theory) is clearly not tenable. The 'field' may be chemical or physical (such as tension) but its alteration by excision of a primordium should on the hypothesis have altered the phyllotaxis.

A second type of theory is called the 'free space' theory, and hypothecates that on an apex no primordium can begin to arise until there is sufficient free space for it. The primordia would then naturally be spaced in a spiral for the apex is growing upwards all the time, and the relative sizes of apex and primordia would determine the characteristics of the spiral. There is some experimental evidence supporting this theory for if the area of an apex where a leaf will subsequently arise is isolated by two radial cuts, then the SNOWS have shown that if the cuts are close together no leaf will arise although growth will continue. They explain this as due to the lack of available space between the two cuts.

There is not such a great difference between 'field' and 'available space' theories and it may be that they are simply different statements of the same metabolic fact (WARDLAW *Encyclopedia of Plant Physiology* 1964) that an initially homogeneous system such as a shoot apex may become heterogeneous and show a regularly patterned distribution, which regulates the site of cell division and so primordium inception.

The second problem studied in the apex is 'why leaves and not branches?' Isolated primordia can be grown in culture and CUTTER has shown that such an explant develops as a bud if it is taken early enough. Similarly SUSSEX showed that if presumptive leaf positions are isolated by vertical cuts, structures which are radially symmetrical develop. This led to the general hypothesis that primordia are circular and 'uncommitted' in early stages and are potentially either leaf or stem-like structures. Later (under the influence of the apex) they lose this ambivalence and become established as dorsiventral leaves. ALLSOPP sums it up 'the results are in accord with the suggestion that the initial stages of leaf determination are dependent on a leaf-forming substance from the parent apex'.

6.3   Development of the leaf

The ultimate size and shape of a leaf will be determined by a number of factors such as the size of the primordium, the rate of cell division and cell enlargement, the duration of the season of growth, etc. However the development of most dicotyledonous leaves is very uniform and has been well described by AVERY (1933) for *Nicotiana tabacum*. Stages similar to those he describes can be seen in transections of apical buds of most angiosperms.

The primordium becomes peg-like and nearly circular in cross-section but develops a flattened side next to the apex. This peg will be the future mid-rib/petiole of the leaf and bears the meristematic cells from which the leaf blade will arise (Fig. 6–1). At first, growth is most active at the apex but the daughter cells retain their meristematic power and later growth is intercalary. The end product of this series of divisions is a lengthened peg which is thickened by the development of a strip of cells forming an adaxial meristem beneath the adaxial protoderm. The consequent regular divisions of this meristem build up the thickness of the mid-rib and petiolar region, and in it procambial cells develop which connect to those in the stem apex.

Along the adaxial margins of the developing leaf, further groups of cells become apparent by their activity in cell division. These are the marginal meristems (Fig. 6–1) which consist of the marginal initials, a superficial layer of meristematic cells which form the epidermis of the leaf lamina, and the submarginal initials from which arise all the internal tissues of the leaf. Usually the marginal initials divide anticlinally and the submarginal initials divide in all directions.

The continued division of these initials produces the flattened lateral extensions of the leaf 'peg' which will eventually be the leaf lamina. The variety in shape found in the leaves of angiosperms is determined by the shape of the initial primordium, the number, distribution, and orientation of cell divisions and the degrees of cell enlargement at different points in the young leaf.

The internal tissues arising from submarginal meristems will differentiate into palisade tissue, spongy mesophyll and vascular tissue. Most

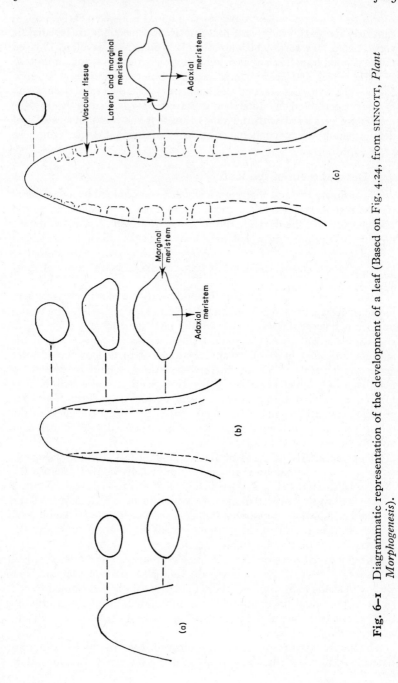

Fig. 6–1 Diagrammatic representation of the development of a leaf (Based on Fig. 4.24, from SINNOTT, *Plant Morphogenesis*).

observations tend to support the view that although cell division ceases first in the epidermis these cells continue to enlarge. In contrast the future palisade tissue continues to divide after the epidermis has ceased dividing and so, keeps pace with the enlargement of the epidermal cells for a considerable time. In the young leaf therefore the ratio of palisade to epidermal cells is 1 : 1 but in mature leaves there are eight to ten palisade cells for each epidermal cell. A consequence of this is that young palisade cells are relatively closely packed. Division of the palisade cells stops before the epidermis has completed its process of enlargement and the adjustment of the palisade cells to the much larger but less numerous epidermal cells brings about the development of intercellular spaces. Since palisade cells elongate and divide in an anticlinal direction, the separation of these cells takes place along anticlinal walls. In section therefore palisade tissue appears columnar with cells often separated along their anticlinal walls.

In a rather similar fashion the continued division and enlargement of the abaxial epidermal cells after the mesophyll has ceased division explains the loose, spongy nature of the mesophyll tissue with its extensive system of air spaces (Fig. 6–2).

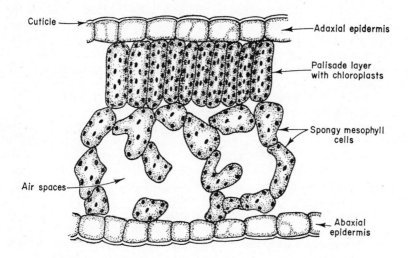

Fig. 6–2 Diagrammatic vertical section of Dicot. leaf.

The development of leaf vascular tissues is not well understood but it seems clear that the mid-vein differentiates even before the leaf lamina is formed and the network of veins in the lamina arises from the central ground tissue in a basipetal direction. Here again there is evidence of protophloem being the first recognizable vascular tissue followed by protoxylem, both these tissues being differentiated during the period of leaf extension and elongation. Once extension of the lamina is completed the metaxylem and metaphloem follow a basipetal differentiation course.

6.4   Leaf structure and function

There are two theories which attribute the evolutionary origin of leaves to either the development and elaboration of lateral outgrowths of the stem (enation theory) or to a limited branch system in which the leaf lamina may be considered to be a kind of webbing connecting small branchlets each with its vascular system.

There is general agreement however that the leaf is the major organ of photosynthesis in higher plants and that its structure (as a result of natural selection) reflects this purpose. Thus in a system (such as photosynthesis) where incident light is a prime factor then the maximum exposure of surface light must have a selective advantage. It seems reasonable therefore that leaves should usually be flat, thin structures carried at an angle to the branch or twig which bears them. This argument could be extended to explain the phyllotactic spiral.

The other main ingredient in photosynthesis is carbon dioxide and any efficient leaf would require to be thin and well-ventilated to permit the maximum inward diffusion of CO_2 and at the same time the outward diffusion of O_2. The same argument therefore can be used to explain the loose spongy mesophyll, the columnar palisade tissue with air spaces and the elaborate vascular system to supply water and to translocate finished products.

The ideal leaf for photosynthesis would operate under the ever present threat of desiccation for ease of access of CO_2 carries with it ease of loss of water vapour. At night this would be very uneconomic (for the plant) for there would be no photosynthesis but there would be a continuing loss of water vapour. This problem has been solved by the evolution of a nearly waterproof leaf cuticle punctured by highly efficient stomata which open in light and close in the dark or when the water content of the leaf reaches a low level.

Stomata develop from protodermal cells which may divide a number of times and one of the daughters divides to form two guard cells. These enlarge and eventually assume the shape characteristic of the species. There is a dissolution of the pectic material of the common cell wall and the guard cells separate leaving the typical pore. The guard cells then become unevenly thickened and the opening and closure of the pore is a consequence of the unequal dilation and contraction of the guard cells in response to changes in their water content (Fig. 6–3, Plate 11).

The physiology of stomatal opening and closing is complex since it may involve photosynthetic, osmotic, and physical phenomena. When first studied it was thought that stomata opened as a result of photosynthesis in the guard cells. It was argued that light falling on the guard cells, which are the only epidermal cells to contain chloroplasts, would allow photosynthesis to proceed, sugars would be formed and the osmotic concentration of these cells would rise. Water would therefore be drawn into the guard cells and they would increase in size. But, as seen in the diagram, the walls are unevenly thickened, so that the thin inner walls would balloon pulling the thick outer walls with them, so opening the pore.

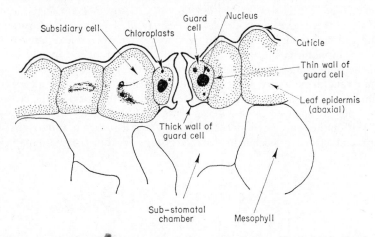

Fig. 6–3   Tracing of Plate 11. Vertical section of part of leaf of *Iris* showing open stoma.

It was soon realized that this mechanism was much too slow and an approach was attempted via the enzyme system. Here the argument was that light would start photosynthesis and CO_2 in the cell sap would be speedily used up. This would alter the pH of the cell sap to the optimum for enzymic action, starch would be hydrolysed and the stomata would open.

The suggestion was then made by SCARTH that the change in pH might affect the degree of hydration of cell colloids. With decreasing acidity of the cell sap the hydration of the colloids in the guard cell would increase and so the volume of the cell. This would lead to stomatal opening.

None of the above mechanisms satisfy all conditions under which stomatal opening will occur and it may be that the energy used is obtained from ATP and not from immediate photosynthetic products. Thus an approach different from any of the above may be necessary in order to explain the phenomena of stomatal opening and closing.

Roots

7.1 Differentiation in roots

The structure of the apical meristem of roots has been briefly considered in § 1.3, and so only processes taking place in older tissues will be considered in this section. Behind the apex in any median longisection of a root there is visible evidence of zones of cell division, cell elongation, and cell differentiation, although there may be considerable difference in degree of maturity in cells at the same level in the root and in cells even in the same tissue of the root. Nevertheless the general picture is of an epidermal/protodermal layer one cell in thickness containing a cortical zone of large vacuolated cells extending nearly to the apex. In the centre the cells are small forming a dense central cylinder (Fig. 7–1).

Within the central cylinder (the plerome) the first cells to show signs of differentiation are located in discrete groups. Within these groups cell

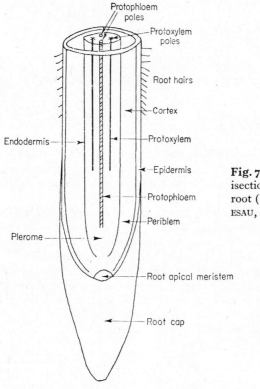

Fig. 7–1 Diagrammatic longisection of terminal portion of root (Based on Fig. 17.7 from ESAU, *Plant Anatomy*).

Protophloem poles
Protoxylem poles
Root hairs
Cortex
Endodermis
Protoxylem
Epidermis
Protophloem
Periblem
Plerome
Root apical meristem
Root cap

division is frequent so that the appearance of small dense cells is given. These cells will later elongate to form typical sieve tubes and companion cells and is the protophloem.

In the centre a little further from the apex than the protophloem, cells begin to enlarge and vacuolate while surrounding cells may still be dividing. These central cells will constitute the metaxylem and it is interesting to note that the metaxylem cells appear conspicuous by reason of their size, but they are not the first xylem to develop lignified walls and differentiate into mature xylem vessels.

The protoxylem arises in positions in the plerome which alternate with the protophloem and differentiation to vessels proceeds in a centripetal direction until the protoxylem links up to the large metaxylem cells which then differentiate fully forming thick lignified walls with pits.

The final differentiation of xylem and phloem produces the typical root appearance in transection of the epidermis, cortex, and layers of endodermis and pericycle. In the centre is the vascular cylinder with its star-like appearance having a central metaxylem joining to the rays of protoxylem and situated between the rays are the groups of phloem (Fig. 7-2, Plate 12).

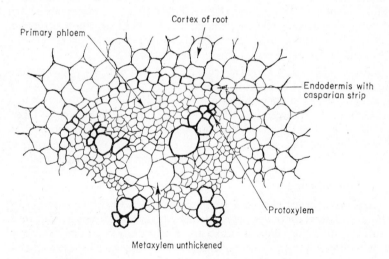

Fig. 7-2   Diagram of part of Plate 12, transection of central portion of Root of *Ranunculus*.

In terms of direction and speed of differentiation the root is much simpler than the stem for the complication of leaves does not arise. The protoxylem is visible near the root tip and the central metaxylem is last to appear as a fully thickened cell type.

Surrounding the central cylinder in the differentiated part of the primary root is a conspicuous layer of cells (the endodermis) with thickened radial walls. This layer has considerable physiological significance.

7.2   Root hairs

The surface of the root is devoid of a cuticle but it bears small tubular extensions of epidermal cells. These are rarely branched, are named root hairs, and develop from surface cells near the tip of the root at about the zone of xylem differentiation, i.e. behind the zone of intensive elongation. It is possible to examine a root tip and see all stages of root hair development from a tiny bump on the surface of a cell to the relatively long hair.

Much research (STREET 1966) largely on grass roots has shown two typical patterns of root hair formation.

(1) the epidermis has a regular alternation of long and short cells and the root hairs only arise from short cells (trichoblasts)

(2) there is no regular arrangment of trichoblasts and hairs can arise from any epidermal cell.

Workers have claimed differences in enzyme activity (e.g. acid phosphatase) between trichoblasts and ordinary epidermal cells but although such differences exist they have not been demonstrated in all species. There is agreement however that trichoblasts have larger nucleoli than the other epidermal cells and the differences between the two types of behaviour is thought by STREET to be 'not so much one of overall activity as of the pattern of metabolic behaviour'.

Growth of the root hairs is at the tip. The wall of the root hair is two-layered except at the extreme tip where only one layer characterized by randomly arranged micro-fibrils is to be found. When growth occurs new material is incorporated into the tip (α-layer) and in the second (β-layer) further back from the tip axially orientated cellulose micro-fibrils with encrusting materials are incorporated. Thus the tip remains capable of continued extension while the rest of the hair has a more rigid wall.

7.3   Lateral roots

In sharp contrast to shoot structures such as leaves which arise close to the apex, lateral roots arise at a considerable distance from the root apex. A further point of contrast is that the meristem from which the lateral root will arise is not in a superficial or near-superficial position but is embedded in the older root tissue usually in the pericycle (angiosperms) or endodermis (lower vascular plants) (Fig. 7–3) at points related to the primary xylem poles of the procambial cylinder.

The first visible evidence of the initiation of a lateral root is the occurrence of periclinal and anticlinal divisions in a group of pericycle cells. The new cells add locally to the volume of the root and a protuberance is visible on the surface. As the lateral root meristem grows it gradually penetrates outward through the cortex until it reaches the root surface

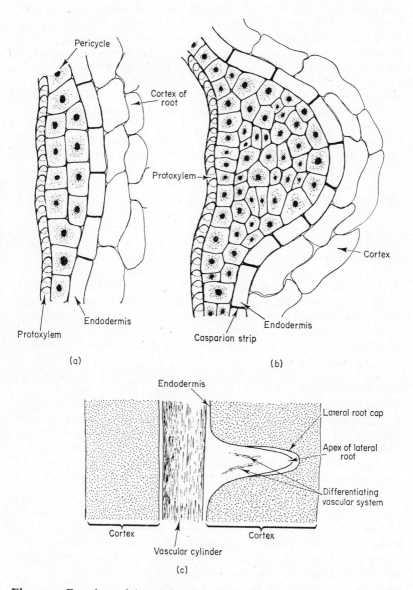

Fig. 7–3 Drawings of the origin of lateral root from the pericycle at a point opposite the protoxylem. Note in (b) how the endodermis continues to divide and encloses the developing root. In (c) the lateral root, still within the cortex, has already developed a root cap and is differentiating a vascular system (Based on Figs. 17.11 and 17.12 from ESAU, *Plant Anatomy*).

and appears as an endogenous structure bursting out from within the parent root (Fig. 7–3(c)). The passage of the root through the cortex may be assisted by enzymic action on cells in the line of passage and of course considerable mechanical penetration also occurs. Eventually there is a vascular connection between the main and the lateral root.

Experimental work has shown that removal of the root tip permits early development of laterals. It is therefore likely that inhibitors diffuse back from the root apex and prevent the initiation of lateral roots in its immediate vicinity.

Conversely it has been shown that strains of *Senecio vulgaris* which develop few lateral roots can be induced to form many roots by treatment with auxins such as 2-naphthoxyacetic acid. The development of lateral roots can also be stimulated by many compounds such as arginine, lysine, gibberellic acid, etc. The hypothesis which best explains the experimental evidence is that the root apex synthesizes substances such as kinins which inhibit lateral root development at high concentrations, but at some point more remote from the apex an appropriate balance between auxin and kinin may lead to lateral root initiation.

Recent work by TORREY and his collaborators suggests that the development of laterals on segments of the root of *Pisum* is affected by light. Almost maximum inhibition could be obtained by exposure of the root to red light and this effect could be completely reversed by exposure to far-red light. It would seem therefore that there is a phytochrome system in operation rather comparable to that found in flowering stimulation (see Chapter 8.2).

7.4 Root culture

The discovery that excised plant roots could be grown in sterile culture allowed studies of the physiology of roots to be pursued without the complication of a stem, branches or leaves. It is arguable whether a detached root is in the same physiological state as an attached root but nevertheless the requirement of the detached root for an external supply of sugars and B vitamins would lead one to suppose that these were normally supplied by the aerial parts of the plant.

Plate 7. (opposite) Radial longitudinal section showing heterogeneous ray of Mahogany (*Swietenia macrophylla*). Note the large ray parenchyma cells on the upper and lower extremities of the ray.

Plate 8. (opposite) Part of a transverse section of wood of Iroko in which the zones of confluent parenchyma can be seen linking the vessels.

Plate 9. (opposite) Longisection of apex of Privet showing two-layered tunica and young leaf primordium on right-hand side, with incipient primordium on left.

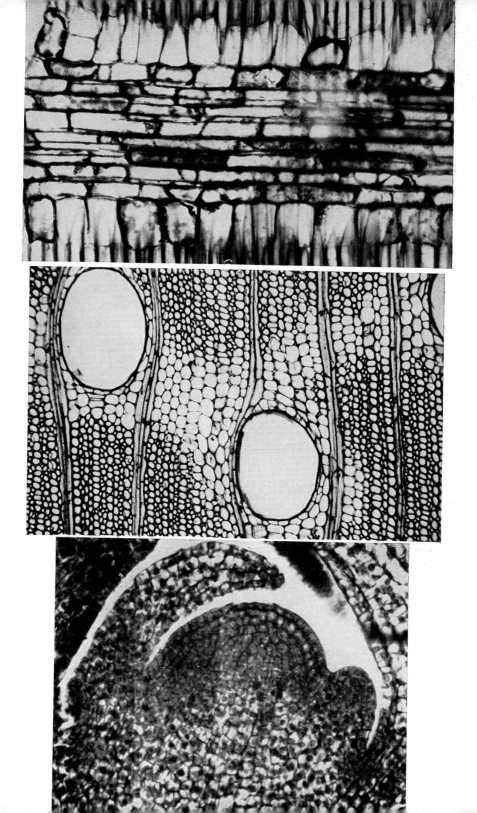

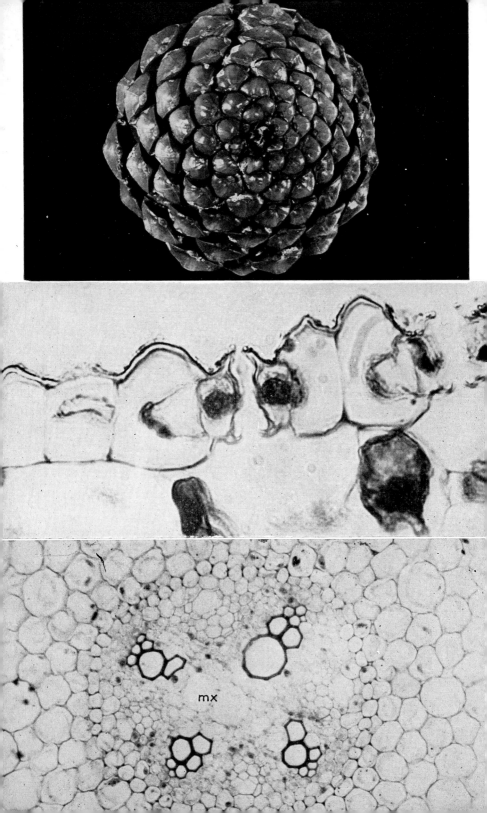

mx

Many studies have shown that this is a reciprocal relationship for since the root is the main site of amino acid and protein synthesis, the shoot is supplied with organic nitrogen from this source.

One function of the root which is relatively unique is the release from its surface of a wide range of metabolites. This is easily demonstrable by growing excised roots in a standard medium and then analysing the medium after a time interval. The medium can be shown to contain alkaloids, vitamins, auxins, sugars, enzymes, etc., which were formed inside the root. These substances are released mainly at the apex, zone of elongation, and root hair zone although it is thought by some that the root cap may have not only a protective but also a secretory function.

The inward movement of large molecules such as proteins is much less well documented for although the uptake of lysozyme by roots can be shown, there is little evidence that it actually penetrates cells but is concentrated in the cell walls and in outer layers of cytoplasm. Nevertheless the movement of such molecules in and out of roots creates the rhizosphere and is of importance in studies of the interrelationship between plants and between the plant and the soil.

Another aspect of root growth which can be studied in culture is the development of secondary tissues from a vascular cambium. In simple root culture there is no development of secondary tissues which suggests that somehow cambium initiation and development in roots depends on the aerial part of the plant providing either a necessary raw material or a stimulus. There is ample proof that secondary thickening in roots is related to the photoperiodic stimulus for if radishes are grown in a 16 hour day the roots remain fibrous but in an 8 hour day there develops the typical thickened radish root.

By feeding various substances into the cut end of excised roots cambium formation and division could be stimulated and this was best developed when sugar, auxin and kinins were supplied. It is possible therefore that these substances are translocated from stem to root in the intact plant and produce the conditions necessary for secondary thickening.

Plate 10. (opposite) Birdseye view of top of cone of *Pinus*. If a piece of transparent paper is placed over the illustration and the spirals lightly traced in pencil, it will be seen that the phyllotaxis is 8/13.

Plate 11. (opposite) Vertical section of leaf of *Iris* showing open stoma with guard cells, etc.

Plate 12. (opposite) Transection of central portion of root of *Ranunculus* showing large but unthickened metaxylem vessels in centre, four protoxylem groups forming the rest of a star and between the rays four phloem groups. Note the endodermis.

7.5 The endodermis

In Fig. 7–2 it will be seen that the endodermis is located between the cortex and the vascular cylinder and it is of little value to discuss whether it is the innermost layer of the former or the outermost layer of the latter. The significance of the endodermis lies in its singular structure and its near-limitation to the roots of higher plants.

As a layer it is distinguishable in the early stages of growth by the presence of the Casparian strip which is a localized area of the anticlinal walls of each cell thickened with lignin or suberin. The thickening therefore forms a band round the cell and is notable for the fact that when endodermal cells are plasmolysed the cytoplasm adheres to the wall over the area of the Casparian strip.

At a later stage of growth there is thickening of the inner periclinal wall of the endodermis firstly by suberin and then a tertiary thickening of cellulose covering the whole inner face of each endodermal cell.

The thickening does not occur uniformly in the endodermal ring, but starting opposite the phloem groups it spreads in each direction. Often there are gaps in the ring and these are usually to be found opposite the protoxylem groups and consist of thin-walled cells, passage cells.

The function of the endodermis has long been in dispute but ESAU (1953) states (p. 506) 'The endodermis located between the two distinct systems acts as a barrier that facilitates the development of hydrostatic pressure in the vascular cylinder by preventing a leakage of solutes from the vascular cylinder into the cortex and thereby also having to do with the entry of solutes into the non-living tracheary cells. . . . Hence all materials crossing the endodermis would be forced to pass the living protoplasm and be subject to its regulatory activity'.

8.1 Factors inducing flower formation

Although there are many different views on the evolutionary origin of the flower and its parts, there is fairly general agreement that it is a condensed branch bearing highly modified and specialized structures connected with the production of seed and ultimately the reproduction of the plant. As a condensed branch therefore it has an apical zone which can be examined in a manner similar to that applied to vegetative stems and roots, and when this is done a number of differences between the floral and the vegetative apex are immediately apparent.

Firstly floral meristems have a limited life. They appear after a period of vegetative growth (i.e. they may be transformed vegetative apices), they produce a limited number of diverse parts and then die. Secondly, light is one of the major factors inducing the change in an apex from the vegetative to the flowering state. Thirdly, the floral apex is very compressed and tends to be flat so that the floral parts appear all to be borne approximately at the same level and not widely spaced up the stem as are leaves.

From his examinations of floral and vegetative meristems in longisection, GREGOIRE (see PHILIPSON 1947) concluded that the two types of apex are not only clearly distinguishable visually, but are basically of two different kinds. Thus, in the floral apex it is easy to see that there is an outer zone of darkly staining cells which he named the mantle, and an inner zone of larger parenchymatous cells, the core, and according to Gregoire these could not be analogized with the usual tunica-corpus system. He named them the meristematic mantle and parenchymatous core.

PHILIPSON however brings forward strong evidence in *Succisa pratensis* that the transition from vegetative to floral apex is simple. In this plant the typical vegetative apex has a distinct tunica and corpus, but the corpus has a terminal group of large cells, a rib-meristem, and a dark staining peripheral zone. As the transition of this apex to the floral state occurs, the tunica becomes less distinct because the central zone of large cells resumes meristematic activity becoming a zone of dense actively dividing cells difficult to distinguish from the tunica and from the peripheral zone of the corpus.

Thus a mature floral apex shows the outer mantle of dense cells which consists of the tunica, and a large part of the corpus, while the parenchymatous core is largely derived from the rib-meristem below the apex (see Fig. 8-1). The two types of meristem, floral and vegetative, in this view

47

are not distinct and can best be regarded as two manifestations of the same thing differing only in the degree of development of certain zones.

Further development of the floral parts takes place in acropetal succession as for leaves, although if the floral parts are joined as in a tubular

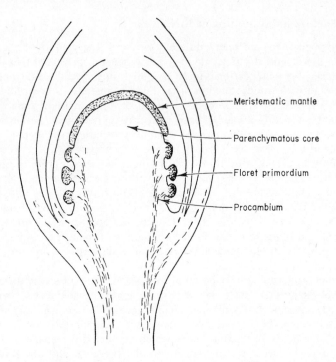

Fig. 8-1   Diagram of floral apex based on Fig. 4, pl. 9, from *J. Linn. Soc. Bot.* **53**, 1947).

corolla the whole may arise as a congenital unit structure. Where the floral parts are separate their origin is like that of a leaf beginning as a peg-like structure which lengthens. It may then give rise to marginal meristems and become a petal or it may have very limited lateral expansion and develop as a stamen.

The reproductive parts, i.e. anthers and carpels, will eventually contain cells in which meiosis occurs with the production of gametes, but despite attempts to cultivate anthers or ovules in vitro it has proved impossible so far to induce meiosis by artificial means.

The floral parts are well known and are summarized in Fig. 8-2, but the forces which cause the production of such diverse structures as petals, stamens, and carpels are less well understood. The phenomenon of photoperiodism, to be discussed very briefly below, can be said simply to throw the switch which changes the apex from vegetative to reproductive, but the detailed mechanism which stops the production of ordinary leaves and begins the limited but very accurate production of sepals, petals, anthers, etc. is only now being explored. Some of the best work in

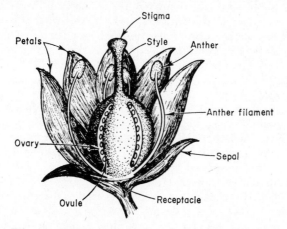

Fig. 8–2 Diagrammatic representation of a hypothetical simple flower.

this field has been done by TEPFER and his colleagues using floral apices of *Aquilegia*.

By means of tissue culture techniques (see p. 56) it is possible to excise very young floral apices and grow them in culture media of differing compositions. When such apices were supplied with the requisite nutrients plus gibberellic acid, indole acetic acid and kinins, development of the floral parts occurred and it was found that by varying the concentration of these substances differing parts of the flower could be encouraged to develop, but in no case was it possible to produce anthers with pollen grains or carpels with ovules. It seems therefore that either substances not yet included in the media are required for complete development or the correct balance of IAA, GA, kinins, etc. has not yet been accurately determined.

That auxins are concerned in the production of sex organs has been known for some time. Work on hemp by HESLOP-HARRISON has shown that in this species plants are either male or female, but early treatment of flowering stages with auxin will induce typically male plants to become female. Similarly the sex of cucumber flowers can be changed from bi-sexual to female by application of auxin. It is suggested that the balance between the floral parts is maintained by auxin concentrations in that high auxin leads to suppression of stamens and favours development of carpels.

Temperature, especially low temperature, affects flower production.

This is easily demonstrated by sowing winter wheat in spring when it will be found that it will either not flower at all or else flowering will be very much delayed. If however the seed is partly germinated and then given a low temperature treatment the wheat will flower at its usual time. This induction of flower production by a low temperature treatment is the basis of the process of 'vernalization' and it was shown that the power to 'perceive' low temperature resides in the shoot apex for isolated apices in culture could be vernalized. Even more remarkable is the fact that very young (5-day) embryos could also be vernalized, and that a vernalized apex grafted on a non-vernalized shoot would cause the latter to flower (LEOPOLD 1966).

Chemical substances are therefore involved and a hypothetical substance 'vernalin' was suggested as the active agent. It is significant that many plants which normally require cold treatment before they will flower, can be made to flower by the application of gibberellin and CAJLACHJAN has shown that vernalized plants have a higher gibberellin content than non-vernalized plants.

The evidence for chemical control of flowering is therefore very strong indeed but the complexity of the total flowering process and its variability in different plants has so far prevented the formulation of a generalized hypothesis for flowering which has been proved to have universal applicability.

8.2 Photoperiodicity

Many environmental factors operate to induce the change from vegetative to flowering apex but the most important of these is light. This was first appreciated by GARNER and ALLARD in 1920 when they discovered that tobacco plants could be induced to flower or made to remain in the vegetative condition by altering the length of the daily period of light to which they were exposed. This is the phenomenon of photoperiodicity which is discussed in detail in another volume in this series. However it has to be commented on here by virtue of its relevance.

Following the original discovery it was soon apparent that there were short- and long-day plants, the former only flowering when the length of the light period (the day) was less than a certain maximum of c. 11–15 hours, and the latter only flowering when the day-length exceeded 12–14 hours. In addition there is a day-neutral group which is not affected by day length.

The situation was complicated when it was shown that the critical factor was not the length of the light period but the continuous length of the dark (night) period. Thus a short-day (8 hours) plant would flower under a regime of 8 hours light and 16 hours dark, but if in the middle of the dark period there was an interruption by light for even a short period the plant would remain in the non-flowering state.

The perception of light is in the leaves since if leaves are removed or covered there is no photoperiodic response. If an induced short day leaf is grafted to a non-induced short-day plant, the plant will flower. From these two facts it would seem as if (a) the sensitive area or material was in the leaves and (b) the result of the induction was the production of a diffusible substance or substances which were not 'species specific'. Further if a leaf from an induced *long-day* plant was grafted on a non-induced *short-day* plant the latter would flower, indicating that the same substance(s) is involved in flower induction in both types of plant. This has been named a 'florigen' and although it has not been characterized chemically it is thought to be auxin-like in nature.

The suggestion now widely adopted is that in short-day plants, a stimulus to flowering is generated in the dark and under normal conditions flowering will inevitably follow. But if the dark period is interrupted by a period of red light (660 mμ) flowering is prevented. It seems reasonable therefore to postulate that a flower-inducing substance produced in the dark is destroyed by light of 660 mμ wave length. If however the dark period of a short-day plant is interrupted by far-red light (730 mμ) then flowering is not stopped but proceeds normally. One can therefore say that although light of 660 mμ destroys the flowering substance, light of 730 mμ has no effect on it.

A further complication is that if a short-day plant has its dark period interrupted by a period of red (660 mμ) light followed by a far-red (730 mμ) light then the inhibition of flowering (which would be expected by the exposure to light of 660 mμ) does *not* take place and the plant will flower.

This reversal of the 'red light' effect is known to be very widespread and it has been shown that plants possess a pigment, phytochrome (P) which exists in two forms, P_{FR} which inhibits flower formation in short-day plants and which can be converted by far-red light to P_R in which state the inhibition is removed (TORREY 1967).

8.3 The relationship between fertilization and seed and fruit production

From a reproductive point of view the flower is a complex mechanism to ensure that seed for the new generation is produced. Operationally it can be regarded as consisting of (1) an outer protective covering, the sepals; (2) appendages normally attractive to insects, the petals; (3) the anthers, structures bearing the male gametes or pollen grains*; (4) the female gametes or ovules protected inside the carpels*. The evolution of the seed habit with its advantages for protection and nutrition of the embryo is comparable to the evolution of internal fertilization and nutrition of the young within the mother in the animal kingdom. The transfer of pollen to stigma followed usually by the growth of the pollen tube and the fertilization of the ovum was considered to be the beginning of a chain of events

---

* The true gametes are the sperm nucleus and the ovum, but these are borne by the anthers and ovules.

which inevitably terminated in the production of the seed and the fruit and the eventual dissemination of the seed. It is now realized that fruit production need not necessarily be preceded by seed formation.

In 1909 FITTING showed that pollen contained a water soluble substance which, when applied to the stigma of plants, would prevent abscission of the flower and encourage swelling of the ovary. Auxin was shown to have the same properties and in 1936 it was demonstrated that pollen contained auxin. Further, auxin caused development of fruit even though no seeds were present, and parthenocarpic fruits of tomato, strawberries, oranges and many others have been produced. This has considerable economic significance and there are very few fruits which cannot be found in the 'seedless' form. Spraying with auxin and gibberellin will sometimes induce fruit set but it is simplest to produce varieties of fruit whose pollen is sterile and in which pollination will induce fruit production but no seeds will be produced.

8.4 Fruits and their physiology

As the ovules when fertilized develop into seeds, so the carpels containing the ovules and other adjacent parts of the flowering axis are stimulated to differentiate and enlarge producing a structure, the fruit. In general parlance a fruit is something tasty and juicy, but in strict botanic terms there are very many different kinds of fruit ranging from a nut through pods of peas and beans, dandelion 'clocks', etc., to the well-recognized orange and apple. Fruits are classified often on whether they are dry or juicy, one-seeded, or many-seeded, are produced from carpel only or from carpel plus other parts of the plant, and whether they split, explode, decay, etc. to liberate the seeds they contain.

Essentially however all fruits containing seeds can be said to have biological significance in three ways (1) they protect the seed (2) they may serve to nourish the seed (3) they help to disperse the seed. It is obvious that in such a diverse assemblage of fruits the above roles will have differing emphases but most fruits can be said to be built on a simple plan. They have a fruit wall or exocarp which may be the wall of the ovary or carpel but in complex fruits may originate from the stem or other parts. Within this wall is a complex tissue, the mesocarp which is often the attractive edible part of the fruit, and in the centre an endocarp layer which immediately surrounds and protects the seed or seeds (Fig. 8–3).

In many fruits these three layers are combined in the pericarp and this may be much elaborated to produce wings or plumes and so aid dispersal of the contained seed.

The fruit stage in the life of the plant is of great interest to man, for many fruits are edible and form a large part of our diet, e.g. wheat grains, rice, oats, barley, etc., while others, oranges, apples, lemons, tomatoes, etc. add variety to the diet and are sources of vitamins. Many fruits are grown in the tropics and transported to the markets where they are sold.

It is therefore of considerable economic importance to know something of the physiology of fruit after it has been gathered in order that appropriate steps may be taken to ensure that it reaches the markets of the world in perfect condition.

The changes associated with ripening such as softening of the flesh, changes in colour and flavour are all attributable to respiratory activity in the fruit and result from the solubilization of the middle lamella of cells, the hydrolysis of substances such as starch or other polysaccharides to yield sugars, and the appearance of many esters, aromatic oils, etc. which are the basis of distinctive flavour.

Studies therefore of respiratory activity give insight into the changes taking place in fruit, and show that many fruits when picked have a relatively low rate of respiration which as time passes suddenly increases

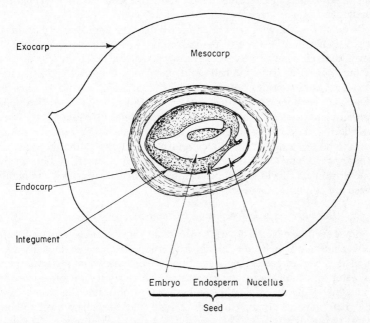

Fig. 8–3 Longisection of hypothetical fruit containing a single seed.

dramatically at a stage known as the climacteric. This is followed by a period of gradual senescence and a decrease in respiratory activity until death.

With this knowledge it has proved possible to delay the onset of the climacteric by suitable manipulation of the environment to reduce respiration. Thus cold storage or storage in an atmosphere with low oxygen or high carbon dioxide concentrations would delay the climacteric and so permit shipment of fruit over long distances. In a converse manner chemicals which facilitate respiration would encourage ripening, consequently fruit can be picked while unripe, shipped in special containers which reduce respiration, then treated with ethylene which hastens the climacteric and so assure ripeness at the appropriate time. Ethylene has been thought to be the key substance in fruit ripening for it can be shown to be produced by fruit and may be the trigger which begins the rise to the climacteric (LEOPOLD 1966).

8.5   Seeds and dormancy

Functionally the seed can be regarded as an embryo enclosed along with a food store in a protective coat (Fig. 8–3). As the seed develops from the fertilized ovule there is a progressive decrease in water content until a mature dry seed may have only 5 per cent water content, and it is this state of near desiccation which gives the seed its longevity and its resistance to many variations of environment.

Normally seeds will germinate immediately the appropriate conditions are available and these are recognized to be (1) a supply of oxygen which permits respiration to proceed (2) a supply of water which will dissolve or put into suspension the cell contents so that chemical and especially enzymic reactions can occur, and (3) a suitable temperature to allow the chemical reactions to go on at an adequate rate. Some seeds require special conditions such as light, etc. but they are infrequent.

It is not difficult however to show that even under seemingly ideal conditions of temperature, water and oxygen supply, many seeds will still not germinate. Such seeds are said to exhibit dormancy. This term is a description of a condition which can arise from many causes but generally these are contained by three categories.

8.5.1   *Dormancy which depends on the seed coat*

Since seeds are isolated parts of the plant they have no supply of water other than that which they can absorb through the seed coat. Many seeds such as clover and sweet pea have thick hard coats which are impervious to water and which will consequently delay germination until the seed coat is naturally decayed in the soil as a result of bacterial action or until the coat is artificially abraded or scarified. Old gardeners used to chew sweet pea seeds or else 'nick' them with a knife to encourage germination.

Such thick coats may also impede gas exchange and especially the escape of respiratory CO_2 and may also cause a reduction in mineral salt uptake.

8.5.2   *Dormancy due to immature embryos*

In some plants the seed and fruit may be shed before the embryo is fully developed and it follows that a period of dormancy must ensue for the seed as shed is not in a fit state to grow. Once embryo development is complete the seed then germinates with no special treatment.

8.5.3   Dormancy due to chemical inhibitors

In juicy fruits such as oranges or tomatoes ordinary observation shows that the seed is not germinating while in the fruit although there is plenty of liquid present and it is now certain that there are inhibitors of germination in many seeds and fruits. Some of these inhibitory substances can be destroyed by cold or heat treatment and this is the basis of seed stratification which is the name given to the agricultural and horticultural practice of chilling seeds. In nature many of these inhibitory substances are simply washed away as the seed lies in the ground.

Chemicals too can remove dormancy due to inhibitors and in some cases they actually increase and hasten germination. Gibberellic acid is widely used in the brewing industry to hasten the germination of the barley from which the beer is brewed, and it has been shown that kinins, auxins, nitrates, etc. will all hasten and encourage germination.

8.6   The embryo and its development

The embryo, although the most important part of the seed, is little understood for here in its essential form is the whole as yet unsolved problem of differentiation. From the single celled zygote a series of cell divisions produce an embryo proper and a larger mass of tissue the suspensor (Fig. 8–4). This is a slow process which is much exceeded by the development of endospermous tissue arising from the triploid endosperm nucleus. In consequence the embryo is surrounded by this nutritive tissue during its development and as the embryo increases in size so the endosperm becomes less and may be completely used up by the time the seed is ripe. Embryos in many different stages of development can easily be obtained by dissection of the fruit of Shepherd's Purse (*Capsella bursa-pastoris*).

Many workers have carefully dissected young embryos from the seed and tried to grow them in artificial culture. This method proved unavailing until VAN OVERBECK (1941) had the idea of supplementing the usual culture medium with coconut milk. This proved immediately effective and embryos were thereby reared to young plants and eventually adults. Coconut milk is however a liquid endosperm and on analysis was shown to contain a complex mixture of mineral salts, sugars, hormones, etc., thus it seems that young embryos are dependent on the endosperm for their supply of certain essential growth factors. Old embryos on the other hand are almost self-sufficient and only requre mineral salts, CO_2, O_2 and light.

More recently work by RAGHAVAN has shown that very young embryos of *Capsella* can be grown to maturity if the appropriate balance of hormones were maintained in the medium despite the absence of amino acids, sugars, etc. It would seem therefore that in this work is a clear indication that the genetic potentialities inherent in the zygote are ordered and stimulated by the presence of substances in the environment and that orderly development may be within our experimental control.

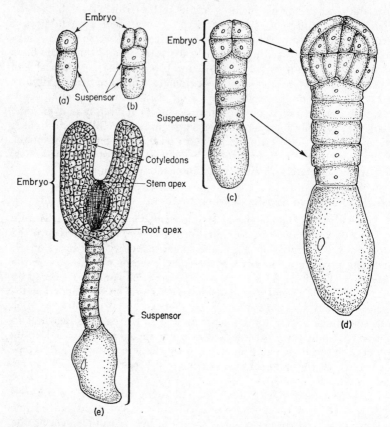

Fig. 8–4 Some diagrammatic drawings of the development of a plant embryo showing the gradual separation into the embryo proper and the suspensor, followed by elaboration of cotyledons and stem and root apex.

8.7 Appendix: The elements of plant tissue culture

Many plant tissues can be cultured on nutrient agar. The major problem in obtaining satisfactory tissue cultures is that of avoiding contamination by micro-organisms. Sterility precautions should therefore be followed at every stage of the technique and if this is done interesting results can be obtained fairly easily.

The basic medium is one prepared by WHITE, the ingredients of which are listed below.

Ingredients	mg/litre
$Ca(NO_3)_2$	200
$MgSO_4$	360
Na_2SO_4	200
KNO_3	80
KCl	65
NaH_2PO_4	16·5
KI	0·75
$Fe_2(SO_4)_3$	2·5
$MnSO_4$	4·5
$ZnSO_4$	1·5
H_3BO_3	1·5
Glycine	3·0
Thiamine	0·1
Niacin	0·5
Pyridoxine	0·1
Sucrose	20,000

It will be noticed that this medium is a list of salts and its efficiency is low unless it is supplemented with 10 per cent by volume of coconut milk. The medium should then be dispensed by putting 30 ml into conical flasks which should be plugged with cottonwool in the usual way. If liquid medium is desired, the flasks can then be autoclaved, but for solid medium agar at 0·5 per cent should be added before sterilizing.

A wide range of plant material can be used, but probably the simplest for elementary work is carrot. The hands should be thoroughly washed and wiped over with cottonwool soaked in alcohol and the surface of the carrot cleaned, using alcohol in order to make it as sterile as possible. The surface-sterilized carrot should be put into a sterile crystallizing dish in which it can be easily broken by direct pressure to expose a clean surface. If the carrots are large they can be halved using a flamed scalpel.

A cylinder of tissue should then be taken from the carrot using a sterile cork-borer. This cylinder should include part of the outer and inner tissues of the carrot. This cylinder can be put into another sterile crystallizing dish and using a flamed scalpel each end of the cylinder can be removed and discarded. The remaining part of the cylinder should then be cut into slices of 2–3 mm thickness. Using a flamed inoculating needle, one slice should be laid on the surface of the agar in each conical flask, the mouth of the conical flask flamed, the bung replaced and a circle of tin foil pressed down over the cottonwool bung. It is necessary to use this tin foil as otherwise the agar would dry out over a period of time.

An alternative technique is to take a piece of stem and to surface sterilize a length of about 5 cm. In a sterile crystallizing dish both ends of the piece of stem should be cut off and the central part split length-wise and then into quarters. These quarter segments of stem can then be placed, cut-side surface downwards, on the agar in a conical flask using either sterile forceps or an inoculating needle with a sharp point, and the flask then covered as before.

If stored in a constant temperature room or in an incubator which is lit, after a period of some weeks growth will begin to be obvious on the cut surfaces of the carrot tissue or of the stem and this, if examined microscopically, can be seen to be callus tissue. One can then investigate from which part of the parent tissue this new growth has developed and can see if the new growth bears any relationship to the structure of the part from which it has developed. The new growth can also be examined to see if differentiation has taken place and parts of it may be separated and sub-cultured in order to see if this has a further effect on differentiation.

This is the basic technique, but it can be varied in many ways by adding gibberellins, kinins, auxins, to the medium in different concentrations, by varying the concentration of sugar or of calcium nitrate, which is the main source of nitrogen. This is an ideal technique for devising open-ended experiments which, although one cannot predict the results, may in fact reveal some very interesting sidelights on plant anatomy.

If seeds, e.g. peas, are surface-sterilized and then set to germinate on sterile water agar, root tips can be excised sterilely, transferred to flasks of liquid media and a study made of the effects of various nutritional variations on growth, branching, and differentiation of isolated roots.

It is necessary that the students should know in considerable detail the anatomy and histology of the plant from which the tissue culture is going to be derived, for without this knowledge it would be impossible to assess the results which will be forthcoming.

Further Reading and References

Reference books and review papers

ALLSOPP, A. (1964) Plant Morphogenesis. In *Ann Rev. Plant Physiol.*, **15**, 224–225.

BROWN, R. (1963) Cell Differentiation. In *Symp. Soc. Exptl. Biol.*, **17**, pp. 1–17.

CLOWES, F. A. L. (1961) *Apical Meristems*, p. 217. Blackwell, Oxford.

DARLINGTON, C. D. and BRADSHAW, A. D. (1963) *Teaching Genetics*, pp. 117. Oliver & Boyd, Edinburgh and London.

ESAU, K. (1953) *Plant Anatomy*. John Wiley & Sons Inc., New York. Chapman & Hall Ltd., London.

ESAU, K., CURRIER, H. B. and CHEADLE, V. I. (1957) Physiology of Phloem. *Ann. Rev. Plant Physiol.*, **8**, pp. 349–374.

FOSTER, A. S. (1949) *Practical Plant Anatomy*, 2nd Ed. D. Van Nostrand Co. Inc., Toronto, New York, London.

LEOPOLD, A. C. (1966) *Plant Growth and Development*, pp. 466. McGraw-Hill Book Company, New York and Maidenhead.

LOOMIS, R. S. and TORREY, J. G. (1964) *Proc. Nat. Acad. Sci. U.S.*, **52**, pp. 3–11.

NEWMAN, I. V. (1965) Patterns in the meristems of vascular plants III Pursuing the patterns in the apical meristems where no cell is a permanent cell. *J. Linn. Soc. London*, **59**, pp. 185–214.

PHILIPSON, W. R. (1947) Some observations on the apical meristems of leafy and flowering shoots. *J. Linn. Soc. London*, **53**, pp. 187–193.

RAY, P. M. (1963) *The Living Plant*. Holt, Rinehart, Winston, New York, Chicago, San Francisco, Toronto, London.

ROBBINS, W. W., WEIER, T. E. and STOCKING, C. R. (1964) *Botany*, p. 614. 3rd Ed. John Wiley & Sons Inc., New York, London, Sydney.

SINNOTT, E. W. (1960) *Plant Morphogenesis*, pp. 550. McGraw-Hill Book Co. Inc., New York and Maidenhead.

STEWARD, F. C. (1964) *Plants at Work*, pp. 184. Addison-Wesley Publishing Co. Inc., Reading (Mass.), Palo Alto, London.

STREET, H. E. (1966). The physiology of root growth. In *Ann. Rev. Plant Physiol.*, **17**, pp. 315–344.

SNOW, M. and SNOW, R. (1948). Growth, Differentiation and Morphogenesis. In *Symp. Soc. Exptl. Biol.*, **2**, pp. 263–275.

TORREY, JOHN G. (1967). *Development in Flowering Plants*. The MacMillan Co., New York. Collier-MacMillan, London.

References

AVERY, G. S. (1933). Structure and development of the tobacco leaf. *Am. J. Bot.*, **20**, 565–592.

BAILEY, I. W. (1923). The cambium and its derivative tissues IV. The increase in girth of the cambium. *Am. J. Bot.*, **10**, 499–509.

BANNAN, M. W. (1953). Further observations on the reduction of fusiform cambial cells in *Thuja occidentalis. Canad. J. Bot.*, **31**, 63–74.

BRUMFIELD, R. T. (1943). Cell-lineage studies in root meristems by means of chromosome rearrangements induced by X-rays. *Am. J. Bot.*, **30**, 101–110.

CUTTER, E. (1961). In *Recent Advances in Botany*, pp. 820–823, University Press, Toronto.

GARNER, W. W. and ALLARD, H. A. (1920). Effect of length of day on plant growth. *J. Agr. Res.*, **18**, 553–606.

MUIR, W. H., HILDEBRANDT, A. C. and RIKER, A. J. (1958). The preparation, isolation and growth in culture of single cells from higher plants. *Am. J. Bot.*, **45**, 589–597.

PRIESTLEY, J. H. (1930). Studies in the physiology of cambial activity II The concept of sliding growth. *New Phytol.*, **29**, 96–140.

SKOOG, F. and MILLER, C. O. (1957). Chemical regulation of growth and organ formation in plant tissues cultured *in vitro*. In *Symp. Soc. Exptl. Biol.*, **11**, 118–131.

SNOW, M. and SNOW, R. (1952). Minimum areas and leaf determination. *Proc. Roy. Soc. London. B*, **139**, 545–566.

STRUGGER, S. (1957). Schraubig gewundene Fäden als sublichtmikroskopische Strukturelemente des Cytoplasmas. *Ber. Deutsch. Bot. Ges.*, **70**, 91–108.

VAN OVERBECK, J., CONKLIN, M. E. and BLAKESLEE, A. F. (1941). Factors in coconut milk essential for growth and development of Datura embryos. *Am. J. Bot.*, **29**, 472–477.

WARDLAW, C. W. (1950). The comparative investigation of apices of vascular plants by experimental methods. *Phil. Trans. Roy. Soc. Lond. B*, **234**, 583–602.

WARDLAW, C. W. (1956). In *Growth of Leaves*, pp. 53–65. Ed. Milthorpe, F. L. Butterworths, London.

WARDLAW, C. W. (1964). In *Encyclopedia of Plant Physiology*, pp. 443–451. Springer, Heidelberg.

WAREING, P. F. (1951). Growth in wood species IV The initiation of cambial activity in ring-porous species. *Physiol. Plantarum*, **4**, 546–562.

WETMORE, R. H. and RIER, J. P. (1963). *Am. J. Bot.*, **50**, 418–430.